THE MEDICAL DETECTIVES
A Study of Forensic Pathologists

THE MEDICAL DETECTIVES
A Study of Forensic Pathologists

Kenneth C. Saunders

Middlesex University Press

First published in 2001 by Middlesex University Press

Middlesex University Press is an imprint of
MU Ventures Limited
Bounds Green Road, London N11 2NQ

A CIP catalogue record for this book is available from
The British Library

ISBN 1 898 253 38 2

Cover Design by HT Graphics
Text Design Ra'ana Haider

Manufacture coordinated in UK from the Authors CRC
by Book-in-Hand Limited, London N6 5AH

THE MEDICAL DETECTIVES
A Study Of Forensic Pathologists

It is a pleasure to recommend Dr. Saunders' new work. It deserves a wide audience. The general public, and even some members of the legal and medical professions, have little idea of the social context in which forensic pathologists work, the constraints which have been placed upon the profession over the years and the personal circumstances of practitioners within the field of forensic pathology. The popular image fostered by the media is of television characters such as Samantha Ryan or Dr. McCallum. They of course are always assisted by irascible and under-promoted fictional detectives like Inspector Morse and Superintendent Dalziel.

This book is the result of many years wide research which originally covered all the professions who have to deal with death. Dr. Saunders has ably identified the problems which beset forensic medicine in particular. The profession in England and Wales was funded directly by the Home Office until the mid 1980's. Funding was then devolved on to individual police forces and the politics of the market place prevailed even more than they had done in the past. This in turn led to an unpredictable career structure, with closure and contraction of the majority of university departments. Changes in the medical curriculum did not help, and forensic pathology became the 'orphan profession' described by Dr. Saunders. Very few young doctors are prepared to stake everything by entering a career in a very narrow field where long term prospects are, to put it mildly, insecure.

Dr. Saunders has also attempted to 'find out what makes forensic pathologists tick'. It is often said that doctors bury their mistakes. Forensic pathologists' errors of judgement are exposed to the public gaze in the court room, and subsequently in the press. Many of us find it hard to accept that we have each of us an Achilles heel, and over the last forty years at least three members of the profession have committed suicide after what they perceived as public humiliation.

Over the last ten years or so, the incidence of homicide has increased considerably. The number of suspicious deaths has increased enormously, and the methods of homicide have also changed with an increasing use of firearms, particularly in the world of illicit drugs. At such a time, it is vital that there is a more popular appreciation of the importance of an adequate forensic pathology service to supply the needs of society. I hope that Dr. Saunders' book will stimulate popular interest and raise concern, and perhaps even initiate more positive action by government.

Prof. M.A. Green .

Professor and Head of Department of Forensic Pathology, University of Sheffield, Medico-Legal Centre, retired 1999 (currently Consultant Pathologist to the Home Office)

ACKNOWLEDGEMENTS

This book arose from the forensic section of my original Ph.D. research, a study of four occupations concerned with death. The examiners suggested publication, but this was not seriously considered until five years later, prompted by my erstwhile supervisor, Professor Gregory. It now needed a re-structure of parts, some new research and much updating; but I was keen to take up the idea.

For the thesis, a national sample of forensic pathologists completed written answers to a set of sensitive questions and a further thirty doctors of varied other specialisms explained in a short questionnaire the reasons for their vocational choice. Selected follow-up letters attracted valuable replies also. A special 'thank you' is due to them all for responding so willingly.

As to the book, my general and intellectual debt will be evident as the reader scans the names of professors and doctors throughout the text who responded to my appeals for new details about their profession. Here, I mention Dr. Trevor Rothwell from the Home Office, who was particularly helpful. Additionally, I ventured to spring thanatological questions upon a motley of friends. Among others, Maureen Russell (a former Head Teacher), Bill Beveridge (a Psychologist) and John McIntyre (a Linguist) must be thanked for their stimulating responses.

I wish to single out two people without whose valued help I could not have completed this study: Professor Jeanne Gregory, my mentor from the beginning of this research to the completion of the manuscript and Dr. Michael Green (Professor and Head of Department of Forensic Pathology, University of Sheffield, Medico-Legal Centre, retired 1999 currently Consultant Pathologist to the Home Office), who not only answered numerous questions about his profession, but also invited me to Sheffield to see the highly reputed Medico-legal Centre that he headed.

I thank Frances Howard and George Paton for help with the Bibliography and Index. I am very grateful to Alan Milford for all word-processing and 'tidying-up' converted text. Finally, recognition is given to the assistance of the Middlesex University Library staff in Hendon during the early days of the research, and to the Institute of Advanced Legal Studies during the stages of updating, as well as to Professor Francome from the Editorial Committee of Middlesex University Press for guiding the book through the production process.

KCS.

CONTENTS

FOREWORD

There are two ways of looking at the so-called medical detectives: how they solve a murder and what it is like to be a forensic pathologist. This book will introduce you to the former, but will concentrate mainly on the latter and share with the reader a comprehensive discussion about this profession.

To touch on a bit of history, many viewers will have seen the television adaptation of Ellis Peters' CADFAEL, the forensic medical monk detective of the 12th Century, solving murder mysteries from such as, the evidence of a thread of cloth in a man's hair or salted water and candle wax, to making do without a modern police laboratory. Further back in history we encounter the Dutch Sinologist Van Gulik's tales of the Tang dynasty in China and Judge Dee, who around 650 AD with his aides or in disguise solved complex crimes by such modern forensic means as examining suspects and using medical experts to establish cause of death. In Richard Lionheart's time, revenues could be raised from the dead with the coroner collecting taxes to keep the king solvent. Suicides, seen as self-murder, were illegal and hushed up by relatives to avoid being barred from burial in hallowed ground. All property of suicides, if discovered by the coroner's office, devolved upon the crown. Inquests were still based upon common sense, so that the idea of a doctor's medical knowledge aiding an investigation of a suspicious death had not yet taken root. Autopsies were not allowed in the colonies until the 17th Century, and then only in murder investigations or for the teaching of medical students, provided the body belonged to a criminal. Altogether in that age cause of death was still a vague concept. An experienced American medical examiner describing the case of one of the first recorded autopsies in 1665, illustrates this point. A man was accused of beating his servant with a club and the latter died two days later. The autopsy revealed skull fracture and haemorrhage around the brain. The coroner and the jurors (none of them medically trained) decided the servant died because he had not gone to the doctor. (Baden, 1989). It took until the 18th century, explains Dr. Baden, to realise the connection between the way of life of a people and the state of their organs.

Most viewers and readers are curious as to why it is that in matters of suspicious death the police need the help of a doctor. We know when the remains of a body are discovered at the scene, the police arrive and a group of people stand around talking, taking notes and looking for clues. Finally, the all important man or woman appears, bag in hand, walks up to the corpse, keenly observed by all, but no one quite sure what he or she is looking for. That person is the forensic pathologist, assisting the police in the discovery of cause of death and quite often a good deal more. But public knowledge is quite vague and we want to know a great deal more about this mysterious medical expert than author or producer decides to tell us. Many a time a novel or programme leaves us in doubt how this secretive crime professional was involved, and indeed, how a doctor got into this kind of work in the first place. The nearest, you the curious reader, will ever get to discover what it is like to be a forensic pathologist - short of qualifying yourself - is to read this book. It will tell you how this small number of some 45 experts, serving the whole country as the principal advisers to the police and the coroner on the causes of suspicious deaths, feel about their daily gruesome work, and very much more.

These (so-called) 'detectives of death' practise the art and science of making the dead body speak through the medico-legal autopsy because the patient cannot otherwise tell the expert how the person died. Even before an autopsy, the dead can talk back. 'All of us gain an awful lot of information by visiting the scene and looking at the body even before doing the autopsy. Over the years one acquires a feel for the deceased's lifestyle and habits, which often give a clue as to the circumstances and the method of their dying'. (Professor Green, 1998). Although often regarded as the 'Step-Children' of the medical profession, these doctors frequently observe things that others do not see and can prevent deaths just as other doctors prevent disease. Child abuse or drunk driving, for instance, are many a time the underlying cause of unnatural death. Although they mostly are, not all techniques need be confined to the dead. The clinical forensic pathologist (more common in the USA) may identify new diseases before they turn into an epidemic. In major disasters or accidents, the forensic pathologist plays a key role in helping to establish the identities of the dead from their organs on the basis of medical records and/or autopsies and may also be able to reveal dangerous designs or equipment. Apart from these challenges and untapped potential connected with the secrets of the dead (like telling ear prints apart or rebuilding a face from a skull many years old), the significant satisfactions for this profession are the adventures of detection, the excitement of discovery and the search for truth. (Dr. Baden, 1995).

This book tells of the fortunes of this profession and how incumbents feel about their work. It is not about how to solve a murder. Nevertheless, some indication is given here how the methods forensic pathologists use differ from those of other doctors who care for the living and whose concern is more for the treatment of disease than what caused it. They also differ from hospital pathologists who dissect bodies but will be more interested in the ravages of disease than the cause of unnatural deaths. In forensic medicine the pathologist is called out to help the police (according to Dr. Helpern, who as Chief Medical Examiner of New York City performed some 18,000 autopsies and has been present when some 45,000 autopsies were performed) to determine whether a bullet wound is a wound of entrance or a wound of exit; whether bruises about a deceased's neck are consistent or inconsistent with some police officer's theory of manual strangulation; whether a burnt body was dead or alive at the time of the fire; whether a newborn infant found in a pile of rubbish can ever have breathed or was stillborn; whether a body found submerged in water drowned or was dead before it was thrown into the water; whether cuts and other marks on a body are consistent or inconsistent with a theory of suicide; whether death from a heart attack occurred before a car crash or caused the accident, or whether the accident occurred first and caused the heart attack...(Houts, 1968).

There is no officially recognised register of forensic pathologists in England and Wales, so that a coroner may invite any doctor to undertake a post-mortem examination for the purpose of certifying the medical cause of death. There are some 45 such doctors serving the whole country, of whom a small number of highly qualified experts get onto the Home Office List. In a typical year there may be 176,000 deaths reported to coroners, of which some 80% require post-mortems. According to past statistics, less than 1% of these turn out to be 'suspicious' deaths for which forensic pathologists are needed by the police at the scene. A Home Office sample survey established that the on-the-spot examination takes about 2 hours in the case of a suspicious death, and call out (often at 'unsocial hours'), may involve about 3 hours travelling. A more detailed post-mortem examination is then conducted at the mortuary for 3 hours or more and later finalised by the preparation of a 3 to 5 hour report on the cause of death. Even that may not be the end of a 'Courtroom Medicine Man's' work (as the Americans like to call this doctor) for he/she may be asked to consult with the police, the local forensic science laboratory and other specialists (such as forensic dentistry), prepare evidence to the Crown Prosecution Service and finally appear as an expert witness at an inquest and a possible subsequent trial. (Wasserman Report, 1989).

As a profession, forensic pathologists are worried about their decline in power, prestige and authority within the total discipline of medicine. Recruitment has slowed and pathology become a 'second choice' specialty. Routines are identified as 'dirty work'; career structures (so far as these exist at all) criticised as to their adequacy; academic departments reduced or closed down. Not only does the loss of status present a crisis of identity, but the politics of 'town' and of 'gown' present problems also. But more of this in the chapters that follow. Small may be beautiful in Schumacher's eyes but forensic pathologists are thin on the ground and overworked. There is, however, still a small band of enthusiasts who carry the profession forward despite these occupational fears and limitations. One such was the late Professor Simpson, fond of quoting Chekhov (the Russian dramatist and doctor), reputed to have said to his editor who wanted him to concentrate his talent on medicine alone: 'Medicine is my lawful wife, literature my mistress. When I am tired of one, I spend the night with the other'. This, as Professor Simpson saw it, is the correct perspective for the forensic pathologist to take. So he paraphrased this dictum thus: 'Pathology is my lawful wife, forensic pathology my mistress'. No doubt, this philosophy helped him to cope.

In my previous research on occupations concerned with death, I dealt with them in an ascending status order: the manual worker (grave digger); the quasi professional (funeral director and embalmer); and now, the fully fledged professional (the forensic pathologist), to be considered in some detail - such as the distinctive nature of the work routines; the evolutionary peculiarities in context; aspects of professional socialisation (formal and informal rules and customs to be observed); concerns with recruitment and career structures; the declining position in the world of medicine; problems of scientific credibility; dwindling recognition of this profession's vital role by the establishment; the disparity of working conditions; the role of 'policeman' in medicine; the stresses of cross-examination in Court; the destruction of careers as a consequence of mistakes; the ambivalent public image of a marginal profession; the strategies for coping with the 'grisly' and 'polluting' work; the constant reminder of an incumbent's mortality; and how death work in this field affects the personal life of members. This profession is not, however, standing still. There is a perpetual stream of learned case and research papers to be found in journals and reports of new sophisticated scientific discoveries - genetic fingerprinting, microscopy, voiceprinting and chromatography, to mention some (and why not have a DNA profile for every citizen in the country, enthuse some police) - which together with recent progress towards the implementation of the 1989 Wasserman proposals, designed to re-mould the profession and shake it free from its recent lethargic state, bodes well for the future.

At the time of publication, scientists were working on a technique for storing and purifying DNA, the genes that make us what we are. In its original form, DNA is dirty, difficult to handle and in need of freezing. New research can fix it on filter paper, purify it and store it for ten years or more, even send samples through the post. This progress is absolute magic. Away from the dramas of crime and DNA's ability to create personality profiles, it is central to genomic research, currently a vast industry at the heart of endeavours to modify and eliminate disease. Readers who wish to know more about the human genome breakthrough and what its implications for forensic medicine are likely to be should now turn to Appendix 3.

CHAPTER 1

THE CHANGING FORTUNES OF FORENSIC MEDICINE: AN INTRODUCTORY OVERVIEW

ABOUT THIS RESEARCH

This introduction is a modified extract from a larger piece of social research recently revised and updated which, very broadly stated, studied selected death professions and occupations in transition, and how incumbents view and experience their work. In common with many other research methodologies, my unstructured questionnaire included face-sheet data (Note 1) aimed to provide the kind of biographical detail which makes it possible to profile respondents impersonally as a group. It was initially my intention to focus on this small part so as to compare and contrast the erstwhile image of the charismatic anatomist with the typically functional professional that has emerged from my data today. But in view of its glorious past, doleful present and uncertain future, a somewhat wider analysis of pathology is needed to embrace these important evolutionary aspects (see Wolbach, 1954).

In more general terms, we do not have precise statistics of the number of people for whom the death industry provides a living. Reliable estimates suggest that near 12,000 are responsible for the administration, welfare matters and disposal of some 650,000 dead per year in the U.K., excluding forensic concerns and such ancillary interests as Registrars, Medical other than forensic, the Clergy, and Voluntary Organisations. Also, it does make it relevant for social scientists to be interested in documents of life and work which are meaningful to the incumbents themselves. Most of us know that the concept of 'career' is still an elite institution in Western society. The term signifies a graduated sequence of increasing responsibilities, patterns and directions, choice and change, and more so a way by which a person is judged and significantly judges himself or herself. We are conscious of what is evaluated as a kind of skill, but conceived so broadly as to include a practitioner's personality, creativeness and social contacts. As a further dimension, personal merit finds support from membership of a professional association whose model displays such main characteristics as skill based on theoretical knowledge, an extensive period of education, the theme of altruism and public service, a code of conduct and ethics, rigorous testing of members' competence before admission, and an insistence upon professional freedom to regulate itself.

THE EMERGENCE AND SOCIAL HISTORY OF FORENSIC SCIENCE

The road to professionalisation may initially be swift and smooth. Forensic science as a regular practical discipline is barely a hundred years old. It has been the cutting edge of medical science's advance from Galen, the Roman physician onwards, whose researches made him known as the first pathologist. Later, nineteenth century pathologists displayed deep humanistic sentiments to add to the scientific accomplishments and frequently came to guide crusaders for health reform. Human dissection and autopsy were not without their taboos and sanctions and the practices of delving into the body in the same cause of anatomical knowledge has seemed alternatively to fascinate and horrify the populace. Nevertheless, pathology had carved its own place to consolidate its professional and scientific role. The new paradigm by-passed the deductive thinking their predecessors had used and replaced it by the inductive method to plot disease. This pathological paradigm then emphasised empirically-grounded causality to push teleological explanations of disease aside. The pathologist assumed a medical policeman's role to correct or curtail the consequences of practitioners' ignorance, and also to establish him on the basis of his considerable range of scientific and medical skills as forensic expert, as a means to help solve meticulously planned crime.

Although women had for long been scholars and healers too, and midwives performed policing functions such as reporting illegitimate births and miscarriages, it was not until the 19th Century that they could study for doctorates in universities or qualify for an established profession. Even then, the battle for recognition was not over, with graduate doctors being looked upon as superior girl guides. But a larger issue beyond medical practice was the right of women to earn degrees and get paid jobs. Earning fees were said to demean the place of the male breadwinner; and in any case, professional work would make their bodies unfit for bearing children; medical knowledge defile their natural purity and a lot of study create neurosis. Where women really belong was in the home. Such views were more than just a passing aberration, it was a predominant ideology for at least a century, which explains also the absence of women in this profession. (Bynum & Porter Comp.Enc 1997)

Readers will find subsequent developments of the profession of forensic pathology well chronicled in the relevant journals (see Green 1974, Wecht 1977, Cameron 1980, Knight 1967, 1985, Mant 1986).

The upshot of all these papers is the extreme concern about the downward spiral of the professional specialty of forensic pathology. Leading members have over the years warned in articles and meetings of the deteriorating position into which the profession has been allowed to slide. Its damaged (if not spoiled) identity arose from slow recruitment, inadequate career structure, reduction or closure of academic departments, phasing out of chairs, the disparity of working conditions, and the dwindling recognition of the profession's vital role by the rest of the medical fraternity and the establishment. That this mounting crisis over the last three decades should have occurred despite the vastly increasing volume of crime and violence is paradoxical indeed. What the patient now urgently needs is a blood transfusion and the big question on everyone's mind is whether the Wasserman proposals, discussed in detail in Chapters 1 and 2, will provide it (see also Bibliography).

PROFILING THE TYPICAL PROFESSIONAL

Having early on provided a brief historical context for my setting, I can now apply an analytical scalpel. The discussion so far has shown up two sides of the coin: that of the professional individuals, their arduous road towards qualification to help shape their own personal identity, their independence and discretional space in the exercise of their expertise; but also that of the professional association, which protects and controls them by its code, and projects its own image to a wider public. The first side includes self-perception. Doctors have it, we all normally have it, that is an awareness of, and attitudes towards, our own psychic and biological person. In my survey, for example, the dramaturgical aspects of forensic pathology work attracted some frank revelations about the subjective experiences of the incumbents' concerned - how interest was sparked off in the first place, how doctors came to terms with the physical dimension of the work, how being reminded of their own mortality affects them, how they coped with their vulnerability in a Court of Law, and how members specialising in the forensic part of medicine perceive their public image and how they themselves are affected by it. Why social scientists have never studied the psychological well-being of this important professional group has to be somewhat of a mystery.

As earlier indicated, I wish to focus on past and present images of the forensic pathologist to test briefly whether the original caricatured stereotypes as conditioned by ignorance of the job and such television programmes as 'Quincy' or 'The Expert' still exist. One of the younger pathologists in the survey offered three versions of what he thought were the role-styles in the mind of the general public:

1. The old Spilsbury Image - winged collar, Homburg hat, Gladstone Bag, manner authoritative and pompous.

2. The Dynamic Enthusiast - endless high-powered technological resources instantly accessible (e.g. the American Quincy programmes).

3. The Introverted Expert - likened to the Marius Goring programmes of BBC TV during 1970-1975.

Goring's role was almost the opposite to the extroverted Quincy, representing him as the self-effacing pathologist in police mystery stories with a dry medical flavour. Incidentally the so-called Gladstone Bag came into literary use circa 1882 as the light kind of portmanteau or travelling bag, but gained prominence as the 'Spilsbury Murder Bag', to include all the tools and equipment needed at the scene of crime.

As another aspect of media images, television producers are often ambivalent about the gender they wish to attach to the role of forensic pathologists. Although the number of female forensic pathologists on the Home Office List is still quite small, there are now attempts to show viewers that women too can cope equally well with this (to outsiders) gruesome work. In the recent repeat programmes of 'Silent Witness' (BBC1), the expert is known as 'Sam' Ryan, presenting the image of a masculine role until the viewer becomes aware that the pathologist is 'Samantha' Ryan, an attractive but tenacious professional whose competence the police respects. Sam, like Quincy, can be sarcastic, but this is where the series differ from the American 'Comfort Dramas', where the pathologist always manages to spoil the perpetrator's notion that he or she has committed the perfect crime.

I should like now to contrast these images with my (more recent) findings, based on a 56% response rate of all the forensic pathologists in the country practising at the time of the survey. Of those that responded,

77% were born in the UK and the other members originated from South Africa, Australia, Singapore, India and Sri Lanka. 83% were married, and the rest divorced, separated or single and 85% of the families have two or more children. As to the ethnic background, 92% could be identified as white Caucasian and two as Asian, whilst by gender division there was only one woman doctor among the total of the (statistical) population surveyed. Age-wise, 26% were under 45 years and 11% over 65, which leaves 63% in the age group of 45-65. By way of religious affiliation, Church of England (52%) slightly outnumbers all the other categories, with just over 18% embracing the Roman Catholic and Methodist denominations and some 15% thinly spread over Non-conformist Congregational, Presbyterian, Hindu and Buddhist. A further 15% stated that in terms of religion they are non-practising. Questioned about their leisure activities, age groups 25-65 list no less than 55 different pursuits of interest or active participation whilst the over 65's engage in less strenuous diversions, including fly-fishing, philately, walking, piano-playing, gardening, golf, cooking, shooting and taking holidays. Although somewhat peripheral to the main theme, the occupations of the spouses in paid work are largely conspicuous by their association with the medical world. Of the 40% working mostly full-time, 16% are Doctors and 24% work in medical or para-medical occupations, as Nursing Sister or Nurse, Medical Secretary, Laboratory Technician or Dietician. One spouse is a Professional Artist. Of those (what Economists term) not in gainful employment (56%) are designated as Housewife or give no occupation, except for one retired School Mistress. An additional question asked the age when formal forensic pathology training was completed. Some 77% completed during the ages 31-40, but the majority responded that further study (such as the Diploma in Medical Jurisprudence) had been undertaken, adding such comments that education is a continuing process, that it finishes only upon retirement, or not even then.

If one could identify a typical professional in the field today on the basis of this data, the indicative profile could well be like this:

a) the doctor is likely to be of masculine gender;
b) born in the UK;
c) with an average age of 53 years;
d) married to a spouse (if working) associated with the medical world;
e) with two or more children;
f) of white Caucasian background;
g) religiously affiliated (mainly) to the Church of England;

h) having completed formal training at 36 but undertaking further
    study;
i) engaged (subject to time permitting) in at least three active or
    passive leisure interests.
(Note: please see also chapters 5 and 6 for further information on typing
and profiling the professional).

Metaphorically speaking, there are of course swans, geese and ducks
in all professions and stereotyping by the media has been fair game. But
more recent snippets from the Yorkshire Television series of life at the
large St. James's Hospital in Leeds (Jimmy's, 5th August 1990, 7.15pm)
gave us the benefit of a realistic picture, showing the then Home Office
Pathologist Dr. Michael Green in three different situations during his
busy working day: first being called to a site with wellies and toolbox
when the remains of a body were found during excavation work; then in
his laboratory, examining slides of the body; and later lecturing to
students, who were busily taking notes. Allowing for his visual age, Dr.
Green could well be the typical forensic pathologist as projected from my
data. He came over as a friendly, cheerful, analytic professional and
fluent lecturer, whose working day was not long enough for all the things
he wanted to do.

But at the present time, this being a few years later, the profile has
taken a different shape. Professor Green has charge of a Medico-legal
Centre elsewhere with five consultant pathologists and a heavy work load
in the Department as a whole, dealing with some 1,000 routine autopsies,
approximately 90 homicides and over 200 suspicious deaths per year. All
consultants have research interests, are involved in medical politics to
some extent, either through the Royal College, the Association of
Clinical Pathologists, the BMA or the Home Office. Additionally, all the
doctors of this Centre undertake opinion work for the defence
(sometimes involving living victims) and attend regional and national
meetings of their professional association the BAFM (British Association
of Forensic Medicine) as well as lecture meetings and conferences.
There are days when the service is stretched so thinly that were there to
be two or three cases at the same time, the Centre would be in desperate
straits, and the police would also have problems. So, increasingly now,
departmental members have to juggle crown court appearances in two or
three cities up to 90 miles apart, and fit in the demands of coroners,
family division and guardians ad litem as well. There is no involvement
in biopsy pathology, but about half of the pathologists on the Home
office list combine forensic work with clinical duties.

How does the Professor himself apportion his time? He does not see his role so much as a typical forensic pathologist but, like so many other aging professors, as more that of a politician spending time in the corridors of power - the Royal College, the Home Office and similar places. There is some undergraduate teaching, but a heavy postgraduate teaching load now, since all doctors must keep abreast of new knowledge, whether they work in hospitals or as Justices of the peace. In practical terms this means that the Professor has to spend much time stumping the country lecturing on child abuse and increasingly as 'backup' in courts outside his territory on topics such as shaken babies.

THE ROOT CAUSES OF THE DECLINE

I now want to return to the profession itself once more and try to discover a possible root cause for its decline. This is a burning issue at the present time and possibly connected with the evolution of scientific medicine and the theorisation of disease. But to touch briefly on some dependent (in contrast to causal) variables first, it is worth noting that there is no bedside or patient gratification and many a student physician may fight shy of 'cadaveric' medicine. Also, our action-oriented society may esteem more a medical subculture of those who heal or operate. American society with similar values to ours accords, for example, Neurosurgeons the highest prestige among physicians. The erstwhile status of pathology as the leader of science in medicine needs hardly repetition and the contributions of science and medical discovery are as significant as they ever were. This is evidenced by a steady flow of learned papers and case research reported in the respective professional journals. So, has perhaps the population increase activated the economic law of 'diminishing returns'....that the more you have of a thing the less you want more of it....and made the concept of death less important and human life less valued in an increasingly violent society? All these suggested explanations carry a degree of plausibility but do not by themselves explain the profession's wasting disease. This brings me back to the causal variable of 'medical science' as a likely explanation for this condition, and the fact that so few physicians opt to specialise in a branch of pathology.

THE CUTTING EDGE OF MEDICAL SCIENCE

But let me go into some detail here. The fortunes of a profession might well run parallel with, or be inversely affected by, new scientific practices in medicine. To pick up on my earlier reference to the once fertile pathological paradigm, has it now become exhausted? According to 18th Century clinical and experimental pathology interpretations, death and mortality (like disease) could also be taken to reside in the living anatomy of an individual's body. Pathological anatomy advanced by way of organs to tissues and from tissues to cells. The great Virchow (1821-1902), known as the 'Pope of Medicine' endeavoured to integrate clinical medicine, morbid anatomy, and physiology. 'All cells come from other cells' was his dictum. Anatomy had now invaded pathology and people became a thing-like object as the locus of causation of disease and death. But the pathological vision of mortality came to be reflected within the social dimension of death also. In Prior's view it justified the autopsy as a method of enquiry; it generated the need for the mortuary as the site of investigation; it structured the language of causation which formed the inscription on the medical certification of cause of death; and it justified an understanding of death and disease in terms of anatomical sub-systems. In short, it elevated the human body to a central place in the network of objects which explain and account for death (Prior, 1989).

If such portraits of scientific development are placed against the panorama of an era and projected into a more contemporary setting, one finds that the present teaching load and the limitations for doing research no longer outweigh the 'negative' aspects in an identification with pathology. Biochemical researchers working at a molecular level and finer than microscopic seem now to compete with morphological and anatomic pathology people for funding and recruits. Nor do they appreciate a heavy routine autopsy load during the early stages of residency, which (one doctor suggested) should anyway be the province of trained 'necropsy technicians'. So, the questions to ask are whether what is now believed in American medical circles is really true: 'that the cutting edge of medical science is no longer at the tip of the prosector's knife in the morgue, nor under the microscope, nor in the images produced by the 100,000 power-magnification of electron-microscopy. The cutting edge of medical science seems to be in the computerised printouts from increasingly complex biochemical analysers, in formulas expressed in the language of mathematics unfamiliar to the older generation of medical researchers, and in the isolation and analysis of molecular structures infinitesimally smaller than the old unit of analysis, the cell'. Thus, according to these sentiments, there is little radical thinking (with a possible exception of computerised morphological diagnosis) in the hundred-year old traditional pathology perceived as just pattern-recognition under a microscope, in contrast to the biochemist-boasting of new diagnostic techniques, which will before long overtake morphological pathology. (Ideas adapted from King and Meehan, 1973).

As a counter to this position, not only are the new techniques seen as less reliable and less precise, but such attempts as have been made to replace morphologists with computers have so far not succeeded, since the latter could not be taught to distinguish the subtle difference in cellular patterning. Incidentally, the biochemists claim to be able to remedy that with the help of radiology or immunology. The traditionalists, are putting up a vigorous defence, however. They say that pathological anatomy, using the sciences of physics, chemistry and biology, must always be basic for advances in pathology, which is tantamount to saying that all new roads must ultimately lead us back to morphology. (See Appendix 1 for definition of medical terms). Indeed, pathology will not fail to contribute its due to the creation of the anatomy of life in the future. There is then (so the argument goes) more 'than one pathway to medical truth and each level has its own contribution to make'. Another question that might be raised is whether these contrasting schools of thought make morphologists apprehensive, affect the recruitment of 'new blood', generate competition for limited funds and in the end confuse researchers as well. (Ideas adapted from Karsner, 1946).

As to the 'cutting edge of medical science', Professor Green from Sheffield University, in a written response to the author, feels that it is becoming increasingly applicable in the diagnostic pathology of the living. Diagnosis of tumours, malignancies of the lymphatic and blood system, and of course inherited diseases now turns increasingly on the use of immunocytochemistry and sophisticated DNA techniques rather than the scalpel and the microscope. But, as far as his own profession is concerned, this experienced professor believes that forensic pathology remains firmly in the 'Dark Ages'. In his view, methods of killing have changed little since Cain and Abel had their slight disagreement, and so the naked eye, the camera and the conventional microscope are the only tools required by the forensic pathologist 99.9% of the time. DNA is obviously a wonderful method of identifying people as long as you have a blood relative to compare the sample with. Even so, the old-fashioned techniques like finger printing, dental charting etc. still remain cheaper and quicker. 'I suspect - although I may be a dinosaur - that it will be many years before molecular forensic pathology becomes a viable entity', said the Professor. (Green, 1998)

THE WASSERMAN PROPOSALS

The Wasserman Committee, appointed by the (then) Home Secretary Leon Brittan, deliberated for five years and issued a report in April, 1989. The Home Secretary at that time accepted the report in July, 1990 and senior members of the profession have been pressing for action since. The Royal College of Pathologists' first meeting of the Advisory Board (PABFP) included a representation of the Chief Police Officers (ACPO), Coroners, the Crown Prosecution Service, a number of leading practitioners from the universities and the National Health Service (NHS). Its aim was to oversee the changes recommended in the report and guide this vital part of the criminal justice system towards a healthy future. As Mr. Wasserman explained in his lecture to members of the Medico-Legal Society, the word 'service' may be a misnomer since there exists no actual forensic pathology service. There is only a limited number of practitioners who acquired a certain level of expertise in the investigation of suspicious death and are willing to apply their skills to the detection of crime. But there was still no one in charge, no management, no full-time employees, no structure, no forward planning. Thus, although there wasn't a 'service' to provide, the 'service' was running well - 1,500 cases handled each year, with negligible costs, no Home Office resources and the Metropolitan Police obtaining the information absolutely free of charge. It worked well as the by-product of a good forensic medicine curriculum in medical schools, where it was an integral part of training for undergraduates in eight provincial universities and six teaching hospitals in London. That was the situation as recently as 25 years ago and by the year 1984, 27 of the 46 pathologists held university appointments.

RESPONSES TO THE WASSERMAN PROPOSALS

It is clear to all interested parties that the downward spiral of despair in which this specialty is trapped, and the various manifestations of an inner career angst that individual members feel, has to be arrested. However, the philosophy of the market and the general ethos of commercialisation of the service, does give cause for concern, not least because it implies competition and advertising one's wares. Hence, it is easy to visualize a hospital to placard its offerings thus: 'Police, Coroners, come to X-hospital for best autopsies, modernised mortuary, speedy service by experts, discounts for quantities'. Forensic pathologists have welcomed the more constructive parts of the Working Party's Report. They have no objection to professional accountability, maintenance of standards, and a discipline and complaints procedure. One of the leaders in the specialty foresees departments and common interest groups in different areas concluding exclusive negotiations with their client police forces, so that a reasonable standard of service in return for a reasonable level of payment is assured, and any attempt to introduce 'cut price cowboys' is nipped in the bud. Another very important and respected senior person speaking for the profession advises that the doctors are generally happy with the Wasserman proposals, realising it is the best deal obtainable in the present state of the economy. They have assuaged the worst potential effect from 'market forces' by insisting on strict criteria for admission to the Home Office list, which will keep out the 'cowboys'. There is also an informal agreement on the level of fees, so that really they have sabotaged the 'free market' by forming a cartel of financial uniformity. The extra income is mainly to departments rather than individuals in the full-time scene (though so far, the NHS Home Office pathologists seem to be on a good wicket, being allowed to keep their fees). Already there are indications that new junior recruits are attracted and that the promise of several Wasserman-funded Senior Lectureships may rescue several departments from decline.

WASSERMAN AND THE PABFP

As to forensic pathology, there are now a mere 45 practitioners to serve the whole country and, as my survey shows, an aging band of experts. How their plight with regard to recognition, recruitment and research in recent years has led to a crisis of survival and given rise to the Wasserman Report has been mentioned already. The recommendations are now into their second year and the members of the Royal College are still vague about how the proposed reforms will impact upon the speciality at various levels in the long run, and more particularly, what will happen to forensic departments in hospitals if the latter become privatised. Following the publication of this report in April 1989, an Advisory Board was formed and operated effectively through subcommittees concerned with Accreditation, Quality Assurance,

Training & Research. But when Mr Wasserman, the Chairman, retired and no suitable successor was appointed, the PABFP (Policy Advisory Board for Forensic Pathology) found itself in administrative limbo, with no one to send the minutes to. Following this delay and subsequently a change of Government, a Senior Civil Servant from the Home Office has taken over with the PABFP resuming its activities via the subcommittees and a Board meeting was held in April 1998. (Professor Green's letters dated March 1996 and January 1998). One point to make is that the Working Party has discredited the label of a 'marginal specialty' (which some other medical people attach to the field) by its manifest recognition in the Report of the key role forensic pathology plays in our system of criminal justice. Constrained by meagre resources as the profession currently is, research at various locations continues all the time, albeit inspired by individual initiatives. Apart from finding the cause of death, for example, there simply is no other skill than that of the pathologist to establish the identity of a mutilated body. Professor Cameron's efforts at the Royal London Hospital with rebuilding the face of a woman struck by nine vehicles is a case in point. Austrian scientists are not far behind in their attempt, at long last, to remove doubts about the authenticity of Mozart's skull removed from a communal grave in 1801. In that instance, photographs helped to reconstruct the composer's head by layers of clay on the cast of his skull, following the latest scanning and forensic science procedures. Tests revealed a rare childhood deformity of the forehead which accounted for the slight bulge shown in many Mozart portraits. A small healed fracture of the left temple resulting from a likely fall was also found, which could have caused the meningeal coma doctors diagnosed at the time of his death. In comparison, Professor Cameron's task seems the more difficult since he has not had the benefit of a photograph or clues that may connect the live person with the damaged body.

THE PATHOLOGIST'S INVOLVEMENT IN MAJOR DISASTERS

Another example of a recent research interest is the pathologist's involvement in major disasters. Dr. Shepherd, lecturing at the Medical Schools of Guy's and St. Thomas's, focused on the role of the forensic expert and the need for trained teams to take charge in the event of such maulers. He also discussed the matter later in the Journal of the Medico-Legal Society. Whilst the country does not appear to have a nationally organised stand-by disaster team, we do have in Kenyon Securities plc a company of funeral directors with a world-wide reputation of expertise in this field. It is believed that we are better organised in comparison with the American ad hoc arrangements, including the mobilisation of expert pathologists, the use of body postmortems, X-ray film, finger-printing and dental examinations, supported by embalmers and staff experienced in communicating with relatives, to deal with property and documentation, complex legal matters and eventual burial. In other respects, the day-to-day work of the forensic pathologist frequently motivates him to write up cases of special research interest in one or other of the recognised professional journals. (See also Chapter 4 for a more detailed discussion of this topic).

DIFFICULTIES WITH THE PAY STRUCTURE

It is quite usual (even if market forces are taken into account) in occupations and professions to expect and obtain some kind of subvention where the scarcity of good people is acute, or where the work exposes incumbents to danger, and/or risk, or is so extraordinary by its nature and the skills required that not many people can or would wish to perform it. Forensic medicine particularly seems to fall into this category and one could take the view that this work might be seen as a national service. If so regarded, the complexities associated with financial reward would very likely be considerably simplified. Taking for the moment a purely economic point of view, there are some industries where services are available but for some reason not used, so that these are then (in money terms) lost forever. A hotel, for example, can never be sure whether all rooms will be occupied; a restaurant cannot anticipate how many customers will patronise it; rolling stock operators can never be precise as to the number of passengers. Nor can we anticipate suspicious deaths or homicides, but in such instance skilled manpower can be diverted to a multiplicity of tasks. The Wasserman report refers in year 1987 to only about 1,500 suspicious deaths (see page 9 of the Report), but offers no source or basis of calculation. According to a BBC1 programme, dangerous driving alone accounts for 95 deaths per week, very nearly 5,000 per year, in which a large number of drivers are guilty of murder. (5th September 1990, 9.30pm). To add to that suspicious deaths and deaths from major disasters would swell this 1987 figure considerably.

THE FUTURE -
TEAMWORK AND THE SHARING OF FUNCTIONS

We are therefore talking about a profession in which a small group of experts have been performing out in the field, in the laboratory, hospital mortuary, in Court, or been busy with students in a teaching hospital; and have given further time to drafting reports, reading documentation, conferring with coroners, lawyers and the police. Through the unpredictability of the work, there is a good deal of travelling involved and working hours are not fixed. It is not surprising that little time is left for research. But now a new dimension has emerged in the uphill struggle of this speciality: namely, more and more functions to be shared. Borrowing Adam Smith's economic discovery, a so-called 'division of labour' has always existed since the role-set (see Note 2) involved contact with the police, the coroner and the courts. But the sequence of action from the first appraisal of death to the conclusion of the work in the post-mortem room and the laboratory to unravel the circumstances of sudden and unexpected death, used to reside in the forensic pathologist himself. Teamwork is the essence of good forensic practice now and the days of the single-handed, multi-purpose forensic pathologist are rapidly dwindling as forensic science becomes more diverse and sophisticated. (Gresham, 1975). This sharing of functions with certain other professions will not, of course, be analogous to a lone Texas Ranger, who operates in inaccessible territory and has been trained to perform tasks normally left to a forensic examiner, although our police in rural areas might benefit from para-medical training.

Relatively youthful disciplines such as Psychology and other social sciences (of which Social Anthropology is an example) alongside the mobile crime laboratories, the toxicologists, the voice articulators, the odontologists, computer experts and statisticians, document interpreters and graphologists, among other scientists and technical people in forensic medicine, are making an impact in the field. How this trend will affect the speciality of forensic pathology is not easy to assess. Some control over the volume of work will be lost and possibly, the legal people (who may not at times grasp the fact that the human body and its various ailments cannot be subject to the same rules of precision as the law) may receive the benefit of a greater exactitude. On balance, this small band of overworked forensic enthusiasts should gain a little more time for research, teaching and writing, an ever increasing crime rate permitting. In contrast to the forensic scientist in the laboratory, who is normally low-profile, the dramaturgical setting (see Note 3) of the forensic pathologist and the profession as such, receive a good deal of attention in the popular media. This has helped to upgrade the speciality in the public mind and accord it the image of perceptive crime detection on which the character of Sherlock Holmes was modelled. Status-wise this would also be of help.

NOTES

1. It is usual for purposes of identification, keeping track of interviews and/or questionnaires, and determining the social characteristics of respondents in surveys, to devote a page or so to gross factual details known as 'face-sheet data'.

2. Social Scientists define the term 'role-set' as the array of roles associated with a given position. The term was originally coined by the American social writer Robert Merton and implies also varied associations and contacts with others by reason of performing these roles.

3. The so-called 'dramaturgical' approach is associated with the late Erving Goffman, an American sociologist, who analysed the social roles as similar to that in a theatre. In this way people may project desirable images of themselves which helps to define the situation and create appropriate expectations. Ritualistic situations are also frequently described as 'sociodrama'.

4. A brief definition of the medical terms in this chapter will be found in Appendix 1.

CHAPTER 2

DISCREDITED WORK IN SOCIETY - A SOCIOLOGICAL GLANCE AT STIGMA AND DEATH WORK

As references to the idea of 'stigma' will crop up frequently in later discussions, this part of the chapter will analyse this concept in the context of previous research in the Hospitality Industry, and more recently of work concerned with death. It will touch on its semantic complexities, the historical meaning of stigma, drama in biography and the sociological approaches of some writers, as well as explaining what inspired this author's research interest in the field. A significant part will focus also on some social constructions of secular anxieties related to death and how careers in 'death-work' may engender distinctive social attitudes and stigmas attaching to occupations and professions.

THE CONCEPT OF STIGMA AND ITS SEMANTIC COMPLEXITIES

One of the principal aims of this study is to make sense of the term 'stigma'. In literature and the media it has in general been given a substantive meaning which is to taint individuals or groups with a blemish or discredit. The late Erving Goffman (1981), an American sociologist, is well known for his innovative work on social relationships, roles, individual identities and organisations. His message seems to be, when he refers to the norms and the stigmatised as 'not concrete persons but perspectives', that it is not the roles as such (however they play them) but how the norms of a particular society prescribe that these roles are to be played. It is thus the discredited roles themselves that attract the stigmatizing blemish. In an urban-industrial society, where a powerful media over time shapes, influences and reinforces values held, people more personally distant from the content of particular roles, may either perceive them in a distorted way or vastly different from that of the incumbents themselves. This has been found to be so in the case of certain occupational roles such as grave-diggers, janitors, dustmen, kitchen, hotel and hospital porters. (Saunders, 1981). High-status roles can also be the subject of ambivalent perceptions as my investigation of forensic pathologists will show. One is also reminded of the concept of 'alienation' similarly treated until Melvin Seeman (1959) attempted to split the term into a number of measurable psychological states. Likewise, stigma is much too complex a term to be used in a mere umbrella fashion and simply pass up shades of meaning, varying dimensions and possible categories in its application. Of the various stigma types such as archaic (branded marks on slave or criminal); pathological (characteristic of some disease); anatomical (natural mark on the body); botanical (part of pistil receiving pollen); and the plural term stigmata (denoting wound marks on the crucified body of Christ), it is the social meaning implying a mark of disgrace, infamy, opprobrious epithet, degradation, humiliation or other blemish, that will be of concern in this study. Even in this context stigma is not completely explained for it may also embrace static or dynamic dimensions, constitute a phenomenon of varying strength and be capable of specific categorisations.

SOCIO-STRUCTURAL ASPECTS OF STIGMA

In terms of its origin, the word 'stigma' is traceable to the Greeks, and refers to marks on the human body that expose a blemished person as ritually polluted and to be avoided in public places. In the later Christian period, stigma referred to either skin eruptions as prima facie evidence of God's punishment or physical deformities. Additionally, many societies of the world have traditionally regarded varying disabilities as stigmatizing and the so deprived considered as an economic burden. Their communities subjected them to degrading treatment by placement in an asylum or otherwise withholding ordinary rights and benefits and, in this way, pronouncing these disadvantaged morally inferior. In the 20th century, however, enlightened industrial societies which could manage their resources have accepted greater responsibility for rehabilitation of the genetically and psychologically afflicted and for those whose abilities the economic organisation rejects. In this context, a number of American and English sociological researchers became alerted to the erstwhile neglected field of social stigmatisation and their published findings illuminated the problems of mental disabilities, ethnic group relations, deviance, poverty, class differentiation and community care. Further, social anthropologists have contributed to studies of contemporary cultures, particularly of the social behaviour of castes in India, of special relevance as a dimension of rigid stratification in Hindu society and the idea of 'pollution', when certain substances so conceived attach low status to those whose work requires them to handle these.

HOW MY INTEREST IN THIS RESEARCH EMERGED - SCENES OF EARLY CHILDHOOD

Early life experiences during turbulent growing-up times may often account for the seeds of one's specific interest.   My curiosity about work, lack of work, hospital and cemetery occupations (to introduce a personal note) is all bound up with childhood days in Vienna during the two decades from 1920 and the depression years. The dark picture about to be drawn is not meant to detract from the prevailing cultural milieu and the rich heritage of medicine, science, music, literature and architecture at that time which, however, tends to bypass a small child, whilst political strife and economic hardship leaves a much more profound impression. The Social Democrats saw their good intentions for social reform endangered by the reactionary 'Green-shirts' (A Home Defence Force) and to counter this formed their own protective corps of uniformed volunteers.   Before long the unavoidable demonstrations resulted in street fighting and armed conflict with many casualties, all visible from looking out of the window of one's home.

Over-shadowing these events was the great world economic crisis affecting Austria, and the ruling Social Democrats could not solve their problems by the orthodox means of deflation and spending cuts. A coalition government was refused and desperate measures had to be taken to avert collapse. In 1931 the most influential banking house went bankrupt and the country was close to financial and economic disaster, this constituting one of the reasons for Nazi support by 1932. Not long after, the Social Democrats lost power to the authoritarian conservative Christian Socialists whose own basis of a conservative social order was by then threatened by their two ideological enemies, the Nazis and the Marxists, with the Social Democrats then outlawed and driven underground.

THE STIGMA OF MASS UNEMPLOYMENT

The above projected overview of general instability undermined the democratic basis of the First Republic and produced a number of serious political and social side effects. At the time of the Hapsburgs, Austria was a melting pot of different races, all competing for the limited work to be had. In the year 1932, the Federal Chancellor invoked strict controls under a resurrected wartime law and the consent of his political party, which not only curbed civil liberties through regulating the distribution of basic necessities, but also prohibited meetings and parades, as well as censuring the socialist press. Out of a population of just over 6 million, unemployment had by 1938 risen to very nearly 500,000 people. Of those who were in jobs, many did not work full-time. No matter the high aspirations of mothers in particular for their offspring to train for one of the established professions, or even for a commercial education or craft apprenticeship, very few such opportunities existed. It was less a question of what career to choose than being in work to survive, and for most of those available for work, any job would do. (See Note 1). Special permits were needed for guest workers, and those working for an employer at home, as for example assembling jewellery or machining garments, received the poorest of pay. Completed apprenticeships meant dismissal as the employer wanted to avoid making increases in pay. Even in those days the lowest status - and frequently stigmatized - occupations were sewerage workers, dustmen, roadsweepers, kitchen porters, grave diggers and rat catchers. Only about 5% of the workforce was to be found in the professions, and study to become a doctor, lawyer or teacher needed money. Being out of work with no prospect of obtaining work was for many a citizen a depressing and desperate situation, with widespread anomie reflected by a crop of daily suicides, reported in a special column by one of the newspapers on every single day.

HOW PERSONAL EXPERIENCES AND INSPIRING WRITERS CAN CREATE NEW RESEARCH AVENUES

Childhood recollections during life in the Depression years of late 1930s Vienna included many personal dramas as a result of the social conditions already described. Existing factory legislation also offered scant protection for those in work whilst the anomic disposition of Austria's unemployed drove many to suicide by gassing and drowning. Such memories, and the prescribed university reading of authors Orwell, Hughes, Goffman, Whyte and Durkheim in later years, provided much added inspiration for my research into unskilled workers in the hospitality industry, and an awareness that the concept of stigma could be sociologically related to certain kinds of work. My project as the first mature part-time student at the newly-created Aston University embraced specific (lowly ranked) occupations such as janitor, nightwatchman, hospital porter, car-parking attendant and dustman, and their exposure to stigma: the study appraised also whole industries - the Clothing Trade, the Building Industry and Household Service, which were examined in terms of their stigma effect.

One notes that, other than perhaps one or two occupations that suffered moral dilemma (and the oldest profession may be a case in point), most of the social writers and researchers over the last few decades have concentrated more on high-prestige occupations, whilst the atypical groups at the bottom of the heap have not been looked at. In the case of the kitchen porter, as a core occupation around which I chose to research the hotel and catering industry (now better known as the hospitality industry), I wanted to discover whether the well-known discrediting attributes accorded to him were in fact an undeserved blemish. That part of the research traced kitchen porter work through some 800 years of history to show how, during successive stages of time, stigmatising influences remain attached to incumbents to transcend events, social settings and culture. The study included a chapter on methodological problems also, and the concluding observations offered some thoughts on a possible re-orientation of management attitudes towards a work-related socialisation process that may eventually reverse discriminating public images towards lowly esteemed occupations in society. Interested readers are referred to my published research. (Saunders, 1981). (See Note 2).

DEATH-RELATED WORK -
A NEW DIMENSION OF OCCUPATIONAL STIGMA

At the time of my hospital porter research some 25 years ago, one respondent described to me some of his experiences in the job. 'The police, for example, often bring in drowned people fished out of the river. Some corpses are large and bloated and have to be punctured before they can go into a standard sized coffin. The undertaker should really do this, but for a small tip such work is left to the porters. Tall people are also a problem. To get them into the box they have to be shortened and a porter would amputate the feet. Hunchbacks present the biggest difficulty because their backs have to be broken to get them into the coffin.' (McIntyre, 1971). (See Note 3). For years these stories bothered me. I also pondered the definition of death, about which to my mind there was a paradox. Blood, bones, kidneys, livers, and hearts have been removed from dead animals and transplanted successfully. Evidently death of the whole organism does not mean the death of each constituent part. The general practitioner and the funeral director relate death to the whole patient, but a transplant surgeon sees the death of an organ simply as its failure to function in a recipient body. Roger and Hillman (1970) confirm that a biochemist's perspective is different yet again, where death may be the failure of a slice of brain, liver or kidney the size of a postage stamp. (See also Hillman, 1978). The upshot of these thoughts generated questions to myself, such as what it must be like to perform sustained death work as a career. It opened up for me another dimension in the sociology of occupations research.

If death occupations are seen as a continuum, one may place at one end a coffin maker or laboratory assistant helping in the manufacture of embalming liquids, both somewhat remote from contact with a cadaver. At the other end are the forensic pathologist and the embalmer, handling in some way dead bodies virtually every single day. In between these extremes may be found a variety of skills spread over all the segments of the death industry from coroners, policemen and chaplains to hospital workers, pallbearers and stonemasons. In my former research I chose four occupations whose work is in close proximity to the body and permits at the same time a graduation of relative standing in terms of status and prestige: the grave-digger in manual work, the embalmer as technician, the funeral director as mainly an administrator, and the forensic pathologist, formally recognised as a fully qualified professional. But in this book, the focus is entirely on the profession of Forensic Pathology as a study in some depth.

Death itself is an emotionally-laden subject that conjures up all sorts of fearful images and engenders particularly for those in daily contact with it visions of disease, contamination, dissected parts and decomposed bodies, as well as serving as a reminder of their own mortality. So the more we can avoid contact with this breed of people the better we seem to like it. It is psychologically a normal reaction born out of the images and the uncertainty of the concept of death and its effect from a variety of experiences and hearsay upon us. The association of death in the consideration of occupational stigma is thus an additional dimension to other stigmas bearing on some kinds of work and I will shortly discuss the causes of these death apprehensions more fully. However, the link between death as such and death-work, and its effect upon the perception of incumbents in death occupations will need to occupy us first.

SECULAR ANXIETIES OF DEATH - SOME SOCIAL CONSTRUCTIONS

The meaning of death has now moved from the sacred to the secular. Instead of an afterlife, it is seen as the final part in this world, so that without a sacred meaning to neutralize its evil, the idea of death has become almost 'dirty' or not fit for polite society. If death has to be confronted, it must either be avoided or denied. A good way to avoid it (and not having to lay out bodies in the home for viewing, as was the case in the past), is to hand over the unpleasant contact to the funeral director. In another sense, death can also be avoided by dying out of sight, that is dying in institutions. Relatives cannot be in a hospital all the time and children are not allowed to view the process in any case. Hence, death is removed to special or specified areas and when it does occur elsewhere (in a train or in the street, or even at home), it shocks us all the more. As Fulton (1976) has said: 'those close to death and the elderly in particular are, like lepers once were, removed from view to await their fate'. Death is a taboo subject in conversation also and many people try to banish it from the everyday arenas of their lives. It has been suggested by Kamerman (1988) that denial is another kind of derivation from the secular orientation towards death and can take two forms: one is for an embalmer to make the corpse seem so life-like as to give the viewer the impression that the 'loved one' appears healthy and radiant. The other form of denial is by way of a euphemism which refers to something distasteful or objectionable by a less offensive name in pretence that it is not so bad after all. In this case the idea of the 'dear departed' or 'our beloved having gone on a trip', is an example of presenting death in a more palatable way.

As to the 'fear of death', Dr. Wilkins (1990) a Psychiatrist, has recently identified five kinds: the fear of being buried alive; the fear of posthumous indignity; the fear of bodily disintegration; the fear of being forgotten; and the fear of ignominious death. A few comments on each of these fears seem appropriate at this stage. Premature burial is a fear that stretches back to ancient times but reached its height in the 19th Century. The medical profession is deeply suspicious of these claims, although the possibility of this ever occurring (if rare) is conceded. Wilkins quotes a number of instances from history of people diagnosed by their doctors as dead, who were subsequently deemed to be alive. Doubters have their own explanation of muffled cries for help heard from a coffin (just a post-mortem belch), of contorted facial agonies (only the effects of rigor mortis), or of coffin noises (merely caused by gases from the putrefying body). Certain states like 'Thanatomimesis' or 'Catalepsy', faints or trances, may revive a sentient corpse to escape the grave. There is not, so far, an absolutely foolproof test for death and transplant surgeons in particular need to be vigilant that hasty diagnosis does not occur. As concerns the second fear, everyone has a right to be laid to rest undefiled. The fear that one's carcass may be exposed to indignity is deep-rooted and primitive. Wilkins has no doubt that the chances in Britain during the period 1780 to 1830 of being dug up and removed from one's coffin were infinitely greater than being placed in one's coffin whilst still alive. It was, of course, a time of grave-robbing, as surgeons could not legally procure an adequate supply of dead bodies for dissection and the teaching of medical students. The famous were often defiled. In Wilkin's words, the more pious a man's life, the more likely were the chances of his anatomical parts being stolen or venerated after death. Among the more recent examples is the theft of Maria Callas' ashes, Charlie Chaplin's body, the attempt to steal Elvis Presley's remains from its marble mausoleum, and the auction of Napoleon's mummified penis at Christie's, which had gone through many previous owners, but did not reach its reserve price. Necrophilia (sexual intercourse with a corpse), a greatly reviled perversion, also comes into this category of posthumous indignity.

Many a fear is of bodily disintegration. People who can face death with a certain amount of composure abhor the vision of slow body disintegration in its grave. Various civilisations have attempted to arrest or delay this process, and early methods of mummifications in Egypt point to this. The art evolved over a time scale since before 1500 BC and often required the removal of internal organs. The brain was never preserved as the Egyptians considered it a part of no importance. Other organs, prone to putrefaction, like the eyes for example, were removed at the initial stage. Female reproductive organs were always removed whilst a man's penis and testicles were usually left in place. Dehydration of the body, as well as stuffing and bandaging, were some of the early embalming methods, but not always successful. Most experts now distinguish between naturally desiccated mummies and artificial creations. Head shrinking as a form of preservation was more usual among the headhunters in South America. The widow of the Elizabethan explorer and writer Sir Walter Raleigh, for example, carried his embalmed head around in a leather bag. Today, embalming is essentially a process of short-term preservation.

Many people are anxious to leave something behind them when they depart. If there are no children, it may perhaps be a piece of artistic or literary work which they can bestow and by which they can be remembered. In other words, the fear of being forgotten after death grips many of us. It would be as if we had never existed, a most disturbing realisation. And yet, as Wilkins rightly points out, in human history billions have departed this world, unlamented, unrecorded and unremembered, and countless will no doubt follow. There have been through the centuries many diverse strategies to increase the likelihood of being remembered by future generations, such as imposing or eccentric memorials, burial close to the famous, or close to living relatives. The rich and the famous used to demand burial in the church, or churchyard as the next-best thing. As a result, churches became crowded with the bodies of the dead, with all the attendant risks to the health of the living. For those who had to be content with a place in the churchyard, the existing status hierarchy positioned the favoured close to the altar wall to accord the deceased the best view of the rising sun on Judgement Day. Suicides were not often buried in consecrated ground, but if they were, it was to the North as a symbol of public reproach. Memorials require, however, space of which this country is particularly short. During the 19th century cholera epidemic there was talk of a single necropolis for London, which could accommodate 1500 bodies, but the (then) Bishop of London was just one of the voices that disapproved of the dead from widely different social backgrounds travelling on the same Necropolis Railway and regarded it as 'offensive'. Wilkins's book makes reference to a certain Thomas Willson who wanted to erect a giant pyramid on Primrose Hill in London to house 5 million bodies in many rows of alcoves and the whole structure to resemble a beehive, but we are not told why that venture never came to fruition. Presumably, it was the novelty of space-saving cremation that gained favour, although opposing forces (on other than religious grounds) to reduce the body to ashes do so on the grounds that this step makes it even less likely that it will be remembered. To deal with the fifth kind of fear, that of ignominious death, one may distinguish between good and bad death. Our cultural norm assumes dying pain-free, in one's own home, surrounded by family and friends (who would ensure dignified interment) and this is probably what most people would choose. Wilkins discovered a Middle Age treatise about the art of dying well (*ars moriendi*) and describes some cases where this applies. Of greater interest, however, are his historical examples which illustrate the ignominy of death (*mors improvisa*), or shall we say, sudden death, which incidentally has become a significant variable in the forensic pathology chapters of this study. A general perception is that Royalty die with composure and serenity, but this is not always the case. Charles II died of violent convulsions whilst twelve physicians and blood-letting could not revive him, but his effigy at Westminster Abbey gives him eternity. Richard II died bravely in battle, his corpse stripped naked and attached to a horse before exposure in public and burial in an unmarked grave. Elizabeth I's body exploded to split the coffin's wood, lead and care-cloth, which was attributed to gaseous decomposition, George II experienced the indignity of bleeding to death in his lavatory, and Edward II was tortured to death. Suicides could be added to this category, but the fears which prompt this act arise from the problems of life rather than death. It is a deliberate decision to avoid the indignities of old age, senility, physical or emotional pain. Wilkins points to mental imbalance as one of the reasons for suicide and in the macro sense regards it as a disease of civilisation (since members of primitive societies have not been found to kill themselves). Attitudes vary with country, religion and historical time. It is in this country no longer a criminal offense. Durkheim's classic work makes this alone a big subject. (See Note 4). Although his work is not under review here, his groupings make an interesting comparison with those of Wilkins, who classifies suicides as honourable, imitative, exhibitionist, eccentric, revengeful or romantic, and also includes an analysis of suicide pacts (illegal in certain circumstances under the 1961 Suicide Act as revised in 1978), and mass suicides.

CAREERS IN DEATH-WORK, SOCIAL ATTITUDES AND STIGMAS

Previous research has profiled the whole 'Death Industry' in the context of four significant occupations around which this industry revolves. It examined the changing structure and the functions of all its varied segments (not previously examined by other researchers in a systematic way) as an on-going economic and social mechanism within which a relatively small labour force of fewer than 10,000 people, active in heterogeneous occupational and professional grades, handle the administration and disposal of some 600,000 cadavers per year. Taking, for example, occupations concerned with burials and cremation, Funeral Directors love to see themselves as truly professional, although the designation of 'quasi-professional' might be more appropriate so long as they have not fully met some sociologically defined attributes to give this kind of work public recognition as a fully fledged profession. Such criteria might include legal support for the professional through the granting of a licence to practise and the promotion of research as well as new professional knowledge. The investigation looked into how undertakers emerged, their fortunes in transition and the ghastly sidelines (such as exhuming bodies, for example) that may enhance their prestige and counter stigma and abuse with which this specialism is having to cope. Case profiles have also been included which give an authentic view of how undertakers perceive the job of transforming dead bodies into living memory, and how death to them is a way of life. The big boys (sic) of funeral directing have absorbed many of the smaller ones and not only practice economies of scale (where fixed costs can be as high as 80%), but also attempt to conquer new markets and diversify into insurance, funeral homes, cemeteries, cremation, masonry, coffin production and embalming.

As to embalmers, they are indeed at the sharp end of things, performing not only routine cosmetology on some 10 or more bodies each and every day, but have also to deal (in undertakers' language) with 'bad remains' as a result of an autopsy or accident, to produce some kind of normality of the visible parts at least, to enable the presentation of a peaceful image to the viewing relatives. The embalmers themselves see their art (and science) as almost a revival of the practice in ancient civilisations. There is, however, no comparison with the realities of today, which involve the scientific treatment of the body of a deceased, to ensure it is free from infection and at the same time giving a sense of consolation to the bereaved until the time of the funeral. Thus, the purpose of modern embalming is essentially a hygienic, but short-term means of preservation. Similarly to funeral directors, there are examinations to pass to gain professional membership. The former see the embalmer as a technician to whom the less pleasant and often gruesome tasks can be delegated. At best it is as yet only a 'semi-profession' without the elevated status of, say, a doctor, although the examination syllabus compares favourably with that of first-year medical college. Embalmers do suffer traumas, especially during the early stages of their training, attempting to erase psychologically their hurtful experiences by elaborate ceremonials at meetings and conferences and excessive jollity during social occasions. (See Note 6).

The grave-digger is also ancillary to the task of disposal of the body. His reputation was spoiled long before the heyday of the (so-called) 'resurrection men' or body snatchers Burke and Hare, most often by the way in which this occupation has been caricatured in English literature, and is today still without an occupational identity in the Census classification. This part of the investigation related the work experiences and self-perception of the grave-digger to supporting case profiles. It concluded with an examination of his social position, taking in also some positive aspects of the work that emerged from the research evidence gathered: its social necessity (strikes have caused chaos in the past); its moral status (presenting a respectable and honourable work ethic); control of the techniques of the layout of a grave (gaining much job satisfaction from this skill); frequent help and support given to the bereaved; working out in the open which is a health factor all grave-diggers have in common.

The fortunes of the profession of Forensic Pathology (or shall we call them Medical Detectives?) forms the major investigation in this book. This kind of work is held in awe by the wider public. The laity is known to fear and distrust 'corpse handlers' in whatever capacity. It is the plight of the pathologist to face the body wherever (and in whatever condition) it is found. Relatives can be consoled by undertaker and clergy, but for the pathologist there is no escape once the morgue door closes, and he is faced with the gruesome task of violating the most intimate individuality of the cadaver. The science of forensic pathology has a proud record, however, and in theory this small band of experts (under 50 for the whole country) should enjoy the highest possible status, having regard to the ever increasing violent crime against the person, as it also did in the years when such charismatic professors as Spilsbury, Camps, Simpson and Teare dominated the crime scene during the years 1930 to 1975. Instead, one observes lapsed chairs in universities, a fragmentation of specialisms in the field, and so consequently a decline of this profession's power and prestige within medical science, where this body of people is perceived as 'non-healers'. Recruitment has declined and career structures are criticised as inadequate, whilst these overworked enthusiasts carry the profession forward despite the fears and limitations. Of course, there is evidence of a regular stream of case papers and some sophisticated research, to counter the image of a marginal profession, but the aging membership and its leaders are most concerned about the very survival of the specialty and the delay in the implementation of the Wasserman Proposals (HMSO 1989) designed to tackle its various problems. However, the hiatus that had arisen through the retirement of the chairman and the change of government has now been surmounted and a Policy Advisory Board, with the help of its subcommittees, is now in the process of implementing the recommendations (See Chapters 1, 2 and 7 for detailed information).

Metaphorically speaking, this industry's various segments might represent the oceans in which my four researched occupations are the fish that sustain it - those that are in immediate or close contact with the cadaver. My investigation observed the scenes and actions in sociological waters so that matters of interest will emphasize in discussion such aspects as professional autonomy and ethics, colleague relationships, ideological matters, occupational socialisation, power relations, mistakes connected with the work, alienation, distinguishing factors between profession and occupation, occupational marginality, ethnographic experiences of incumbents, self-perceptions relative to the nature of death work and most of all the association of the work activities with stigma and the forces that tend to counteract it. But to round off that introductory picture there is yet another connection, namely that with the fear of death briefly to touch upon, which I would call the 'integrity of the species'. It demonstrates how some such fears and death work are directly related, and how this link provides the basis for branding such occupations with the 'Mark of Cain'. (See Note 5).

One could postulate firstly that stigma is a phenomenon that derives directly from the need of a species to survive, where the term 'survival' may be taken to include the propagation and preservation of life, and the capability to perform such normal activities as are a part of it, if that species is not to be stigmatized by other species. It would further include the need to ward off predators (harmful germs, perhaps), the ability to reproduce, to be able to maintain the quality of one's life and the endeavour to avoid mutation of the species. A second postulate, (one could argue) may be that many stigmas do not necessarily spring from a rational or higher part of the brain, but can come from one's subconscious and give rise in humans to feelings of discomfort or threat. Thus instinctively, and often irrationally, our perceptions are (for example), that a depressive can't fend for himself, that the violent harms the quality of life, the ugly interferes with the physical form, and the dirty and germ-laden contaminates others. Similarly scientists are stigmatized because they dissect facts (inventing the bomb), which suggests they care more about facts than the well-being of people. Some Darwinian associations in this reasoning are not denied. Translating the, at least partial, irrationality of such public views into an occupational perspective of death work, a forensic pathologist may be labelled psychopath or weirdo, who wants many bodies to cut up; the funeral director may be seen as rejoicing in the good fortune of his booming business at what is after all traumatic for his clients, competing moreover with other undertakers for bodies and exploiting the bereaved with overpriced funerals, although being kind to them as the clients of the future. Similarly, the embalmer, like Dracula, is then perceived as draining blood from bodies, pumping formaldehyde into them (extracted from boiling ants), as more interested in their appearance than medical value, and as contaminating others by the neglect of protective action, whilst the grave digger, devoid of intelligence and possessing the same skills as a murderer, then tries to hide the body.

Clearly folk wisdom (the social) and not infrequently mild phobias (the psychological) make people receptive to certain, not always rational, culturally-adopted assumptions about death.   In communication and interaction with others these beliefs and fears are acted out by a general public actively dissociating itself from particular social contacts (or at least feeling apprehensive of them) when dealing with members of particular social groups.   With the death occupations, stigmas therefore result from irrational fears and attitudes - 'they all want my body' - which is not to say that members in these occupations do not experience similar fears and perceptions about death themselves.   Although not within the premise of this study, one is aware of the connection between cultural and genetic phenomena with their many complexities still unsolved.   Instinctive fears surface in the mind of a lay public as soon as work connected with death is mentioned, well before the same public reflects upon the necessity and usefulness of these jobs.

NOTES

1.   This brings to mind a well-known study by a group of Viennese social scientists entitled 'The Unemployed of Marienthal' (1932) translated into many languages and still a standard teaching aid in many social science schools around the world.

2.   Conrad Saunders (1981), Social Stigma of Occupations: The Lower Grade Worker in Service Organisations, Gower.   This book was based on the Aston University Thesis under the title of Occupational Stigmatization in the British Hotel and Catering Industry for an M.Phil. and completed in 1976.

3.   John McIntyre (1971-2000), continuing exchange of letters with an old friend who in his younger years (circa 1938/9) worked as washer of dead bodies and grave-digger.   He is now self-employed in Hamburg as translator and linguist for international and other patent agencies and industrial undertakings.

4. Durkheim used official statistics for his analysis about a hundred years ago to demonstrate that suicide is attributable to social rather than to individual phenomena. He identified three main types of suicide corresponding in each case to special social situations: the altruistic (relating to the old and infirm, or suicides of honour); the egoistic (affecting an individual ethos); and the anomic (where an an individual experiences either normlessness or conflicting individual norms).

5. This quotation relates to the famous legend about the eldest son of Adam who killed his brother Abel. According to Gen. 4, the first act of fratricide. Related to occupations, Cain became a fugitive thereafter and moved with wife to Nod where a son, Enoch, was born to them. The genealogy which follows sets the descent from Cain to Lamech and their occupations of cattle keepers, musicians, and workers in metal. The quotation is further discussed in the original thesis Appendix Part 2, dealing with the Origins of Stigma on pages 3-5.

6. Careers in death-work include what is often seen as ghastly sidelines, indicating undertaker and embalmer involvement in disaster work. The register of volunteers which Kenyon and other funeral directors keep enables a team to be assembled in any emergency with some speed. The rota does not require a particular embalmer or funeral director employee more than once or twice a year and payment is made as if not absent from normal employment. The cost is thus borne by the respective employer unless the volunteer is self-employed (in which case there may be some reluctance to undertake this task unless reimbursed in some way).

CHAPTER 3

THE FORENSIC PATHOLOGIST - AN ORPHAN PROFESSION?

THE DISTINCTIVE NATURE OF FORENSIC PATHOLOGY WORK

Put in most crude terms, the grave-digger normally neither sees a dead body nor handles it; the funeral director may see it but doesn't handle it; the embalmer handles it but doesn't cut it up; that is a task delegated to the forensic pathologist. Moreover, unlike a medical student, he cannot select his cadavers and has to process them as they come. In this respect the work differs also from that of undertaking, which can be said to be to some extent seasonal and capable of forward planning. Also unlike the former, who are classed as manual and quasi-professional, the forensic doctor is recognised as a fully-fledged professional member of the medical fraternity who is called in to establish 'cause' in cases of sudden or unnatural death, as one of the main activities generally known as 'homicide'. The term covers the offences of murder, manslaughter, infanticide, and certain other offences causing death excluded from published crime statistics unless the police classifies them as homicide. To indicate briefly the volume of such work, there were in the year 1987 some 300 cases of death by reckless driving recorded by the police, but not included in the homicide figures. In that year, the recorded 685 homicides represent a higher number than in any earlier year. Figures vary since, for example, one person can cause multiple homicide (e.g. the Hungerford incident where one single act accounted for 16 homicides). Despite the variations between years, the overall trend is upwards, the 1978-1987 figure representing a 25% increase over the previous 10 years. Over the same period, the number of other 'more serious offences' of violence against the person increased by almost two-fifths, including attempted murder, child destruction, reckless driving, wounding to endanger life, arson causing injury, and rape. Thus, in the year 1987, the grand total of cases involving forensic skills was 9,178, or 204 cases for each of the 45 forensic pathologists in the country at this time. (Home Office Statistics, 1987).

The Home Office figures in England and Wales for the next 10 years (1988-1997) are even more revealing. Notifiable offences of more serious violence as recorded by the police have almost doubled. Homicides are up and cases of rape are alarmingly also up. Only the number of deaths caused by reckless driving has seen a downward trend during the last few years as the updated statistics show us below.

Notifiable Offences recorded by the Police for England and Wales

Year	1	2	3	4
1988	12,772	624	339	2,855
1989	13,926	641	393	3,305
1990	14,655	669	419	3,391
1991	15,829	725	416	4,045
1992	17,799	687	277	4,142
1993	17,999	670	292	4,589
1994	19,563	726	278	5,032
1995	19,151	745	242	5,136
1996	22,423	679	320	5,990
1997	23,581	739	291	6,628

Codes   1. More serious violence
             2. Homicide
             3. Causing death by reckless driving
             4. Rape

Recent additional information from the Home Office Crime Statistics and Immigration Units for the year 1997 is that of 190,349 deaths reported to the Coroner of which 123,015 required post mortems. This appears to indicate that the work involving forensic skills is still increasing.   (Home Office Statistics, 1999)

STAFFING AND WORKLOAD

Whereas the 1950s could point to well-staffed University departments in the principal cities of this country, the 1960s showed an alarming change.   Death and retirement vacancies remained unfilled, the departments of Bristol and Manchester were phased out, Sheffield, Newcastle, Birmingham and Liverpool each had but one single pathologist, Leeds retained one chair, although with a much depleted staff. The London departments were also reduced. In Scotland, Dundee and Aberdeen remained 'one-man bands', whilst the chairs of Edinburgh and Glasgow had been only recently filled after periods of uncertainty. That situation left large areas of Great Britain entirely without full-time forensic pathologists. For example, Lancashire was served during these years by a group of general hospital pathologists who took turns to provide cover for Home Office work. The West of England and the greater part of Wales were in a similar situation. Suspicious deaths in these areas were adequately investigated and the competence and enthusiasm of local Home Office pathologists beyond reproach, but they coped with hospital workloads which increased annually and the leaders of the profession warned of a not-too-distant future where valuable time might be lost before the services of a pathologist could be obtained. Things were little better in the areas nominally covered by University departments.

By 1974 there were only 16 full-time forensic pathologists in the whole of England. Ranks had been depleted by three tragic deaths and it was feared that stress could well produce further casualties unless circumstances improved. Recruitment to all the specialised branches of pathology fell short, attributed in the forensic field to irregular hours, and the lack of 'perks' (since most of the Universities appropriated all the fees earned). Opportunities for research were lacking also, with funds in short supply and Universities barely able to maintain their stocks of equipment at accepted levels in the relatively small departments, let alone purchase the specialised ones needed for the most basic research. Even had such funds emerged, existing staff would not have found the time to devote to their projects adequately. Dr. Green (now Professor Green) describes the work load thus:

> 'Pathologists in University departments frequently have to undertake journeys of 80 miles or more to the scene of an incident, often at night, after having done four or five routine coroners' autopsies, prepared and given lectures, and reported trays of histological slides. Worse, the pathologist in these circumstances knows all too well that, after returning home with the milkman, he will face another day of 'routine' autopsies, lectures, court appearances, and slides to report. Weekends bring little respite. Friday and Saturday nights are often the busiest of the week. One cannot expect men working under these conditions to bring to an incident the acuity and percipience which the investigators and the public have a right to expect.....the concept of the University department as a 'centre of

excellence' faded for most of us many years ago, as we disappear behind trays of routine reports, witness orders, notes in preparation for undergraduate teaching, post-graduate lectures, and the ever-increasing output of administrative departments.'

(Criminology, 1974)

The observations in this part show very clearly a declining trend in the recognition of this specialty upon the disappearance of such earlier medical detectives and household names as Spilsbury, Glaister, Camps and Simpson from the scene, and an acute worsening of the conditions pathologists work under. Why this occurred will be analysed in a later section of this chapter. In the context of work routines, the next section will focus upon the structural division within this profession, the role a hospital plays in the work environment and the support that it gives to forensic pathology.

STRUCTURAL COMPLEXITIES IN STATUS AND PRESTIGE RATINGS

I shall begin this part with outlining the complexities, at least to those who are not in the main stream of practising forensic pathologists. It was thought that the best way to probe questions of incumbency, status and prestige would be to tackle the leaders in the profession for some answers in addition to the data that emerged from the responses to my questionnaires. An investigating outsider will find a highly confusing career structure (to be subject of a detailed discussion later) and doctors in this specialty to be doing work with students, performing duties in regional or provincial hospitals, serving the police and the coroner, and acting as a forensic witness in Court. Some of this work is full-time, some part-time and there are a variety of sub-groups within this specialty to influence status, prestige and pay. Over and above these ambiguities, the list of fellows and members of the British Association of Forensic Medicine displays no less than 47 different sets of letters after their names to depict directly relevant and subsidiary qualifications of an academic or professional nature. One might therefore conclude that medical and social status would differ according to whether: a particular doctor is a pathologist; is a forensic pathologist; works in a teaching hospital; is a consultant; holds particular qualifications; works for the Home Office, the Coroner, the Police; works full-time or part-time; works for the NHS; is self-employed; obtains special fees and merit awards; has laboratory back-up;   deals with easier or more difficult autopsies;   is a defence or prosecution pathologist;   is good at coping with cross-examination;   is called in to give a second opinion;   is legally qualified;   has published books and articles, and/or given public lectures;   has special histological training;   whether such training was gained at a prestigious institution;   whether the doctor has contributed to new knowledge by research and whether such criteria as seniority influence his (or her) professional standing.

UNRAVELLING THE PATTERN OF INCUMBENCY AND STATUS AMBIGUITY

Professors Mant, Knight and Green as respondents helped to clarify the position. Forensic pathologists deal with the legal aspects of medicine and will investigate cases of sudden and suspicious deaths. Most forensic pathological work deals with autopsies on behalf of the Coroner in cases where the doctor in charge of a case cannot issue a death certificate or the death is unnatural. The majority of such deaths are examined by N.H.S. pathologists, many of whom are in full-time employment. They are paid by the Coroner for each case they deal with and these payments are fixed centrally. It seems that the unsocial times of being called out or the difficulty of a case bear no direct relationship in the payment. If the case is one of homicide or it is suspected that homicide may be involved, a full-time forensic pathologist or pathologist with Home Office recognition (often employed by the N.H.S.) is called out. These are pathologists who have special experience in dealing with criminal cases. Full-time forensic pathologists also hold university appointments. The terms of their employment in the university vary. If they are full-time salaried, the fees they receive (after deduction of expenses) will be paid to the university. If they are part-time, they may keep all or a proportion of their fees. It is recommended that Coroners' autopsies are performed only by consultant pathologists, although in teaching hospitals lecturers in forensic medicine will carry out autopsies, under the aegis of the head of their department. When an appointment is advertised it usually contains a well-defined job description for the particular discipline of pathology. Of the three possibilities, e.g. N.H.S. employment, university employment and self-employment, the latter is rare as it is essential to have laboratory back-up. All pathologists must be doctors with special training after qualifying and be registered as pathologists. Five years' work in a recognised institution must have been undertaken and the final examination passed before the

Royal College will accept applicants into membership. The specialist in the legal aspects of pathology is usually a consultant or member of a forensic unit if the work includes Coroners' autopsies. Pathologists do not work for the Home Office as such, but are recognised by it, and if this is the case, they may use the designation 'Home Office Pathologist'. He or she then appears on the Home Office list, invariably works for the Coroner, may be called in by the police and receives fees from both, whether employed by the N.H.S. or not. Being on the Home Office list is clearly status-enhancing and the extra fees earned cause more than a little heartburning among other forensic pathologists.

Forensic pathologists not working in London may also be on the Home Office list but the police may employ a specialist in a homicide or suspicious case who is not on this list. Pathologists may appear for either defence or prosecution. Whether they enjoy this experience or fear it, are good at it or otherwise, is purely a personal matter but can at times have serious career implications. They may also be called upon to give a second opinion. Those employed in teaching hospitals are usually responsible for the majority of published works and produce papers in forensic and other journals. They teach undergraduates and postgraduates and may also give the occasional public lecture. If a doctor specialises in Histopathology, then he or she will be more concerned with the microscopical examination of tissues, which is a specialty of its own.

QUALIFICATIONS

The qualifications essential to forensic pathology at Consultant level are either membership or fellowship of the Royal College of Pathologists. Most of the forensic pathologists also hold the Diploma in Medical Jurisprudence. Other pathology and general medical qualifications are described by Professor Green as 'luxury' items, collected along the way. The basic registered medical qualifications (M.B., Ch.B., B.S., L.R.C.P., M.R.C.S., and L.M.S.S.A.) will be defined in chapter 4. Other examinations sometimes taken by forensic pathologists are the M.D. or a Ph.D. On the face of it, the status of a forensic pathologist would appear to depend on the terms of his/her appointment, experience (evidently bound up with Home Office listing) and to some extent upon degrees gained and learned writings produced. Also evident, but not so overtly expressed, are the grievances connected with extra fees and merit awards. Additional problems have been found to relate to an unsatisfactory career structure, distorted presentation of the profession in the media, the general volume of work, and (as one Histopathologist expressed it in a letter), serious doubts as to whether forensic pathology is any longer 'viable as a separate scientific discipline'. All this is over and above some further distinctly sociological questions concerned with intra-specialty prestige ratings and the extra medical label as a 'non-healer'. The denigration of the discipline and its position as a so-called 'marginal medical specialty' will later be discussed in some depth. At this stage, the hospital as the principal workplace of the forensic pathologist (apart from his/her peripatetic duties), and the role of the mortuary will be focused upon. This will be followed by some essentially biographical considerations relating to the profession itself to show how its future is projected from its past.

THE HOSPITAL SETTING - A PATHOLOGIST'S SECOND HOME?

Hospitals are frequently likened to hotels for the temporary hospitality they offer. They are also seen by sociologists as a kind of bureaucratic organisation that is neither completely open nor rigidly closed. Whether such a setting is seen as semi-total (Goffman has referred to Asylums as Total Institutions) or relatively open, it is one on which pathologists depend as their operational base. The laboratory block will in most teaching hospitals also house the so-called 'department of morbid anatomy', with their interdependent regions - the Mortuary, Post-Mortem Room, Histology and Pathology Laboratories, the Coroner's Office and a Chapel of Rest. As Ashley (1987) so aptly puts it: 'the emperor is untouched by the macabre nature of his domain and is an exuberant, aggressive professor of considerable eminence, who unreservedly claims the title of head of department and exercises (usually) a benevolent dictatorship over the number of N.H.S. consultants and juniors.' In Ashley's hospital, the mortuary can hold 54 bodies, although there may only be between 6 and 10 occupants at any one time to form the steady trickle of traffic victims from Accident & Emergency as well as all the other sudden and suspicious deaths from the community within the jurisdiction of the coroner. Many ward deaths may also have to be reported to the coroner if an accident or medical mishap, alcohol or drug, contributed to the cause of death, or where death has occurred soon after admission so that there was no chance to diagnose the cause. Even if there is no coroner involvement, the pathology professor is keen to have as many cadavers as possible submitted to the post-mortem room for examination and it is policy at such hospitals for a house officer to seek permission from the grieving family to perform an 'anatomical or pathological audit'. The two-fold rationale for this given is 'to ensure that everything possible has been done and to widen the knowledge base'. Housemen don't like this task and some 80% of the non-coroner cases (aged and ailing patients) are refused by the relatives on the grounds that 'he/she has been through enough'. Ashley's reliable statistic is that 900 necropsies are performed annually at his hospital, of which about 50% are coroners' cases.

CORPSE BUREAUCRACY IN THE MORTUARY

One of the hospital buildings (usually unidentified) will house the mortuary where pathology personnel spend a good deal of their time. The MOH Building Regulations (No. 20, 1963) recommend separate access to the various parts by users of the dissecting room (Post-Mortem Room), body store, offices, chapel and waiting room, so that visitors do not lose themselves in forbidden territory (MOH 20:15). In Knight's Post-Mortem Technician's Handbook (1984), the mortuary's location should be kept secret from public view also to avoid upsetting patients and keep curious onlookers away. In Prior's interpretation (1987), the separation of functions within the mortuary also expresses the isolation of death in general. The mortuary is no longer a part of life, and like the cemetery before it, is placed beyond a town's boundaries. Still, the activities within have an important impact on the living. Identification of bodies (and parts of bodies) is a vital daily routine, with the Register representing the focal point for recording all the minute details that are known about the cadaver by those who are concerned with bringing bodies to the mortuary. The body gets a reference number and identification tag. If death occurred from radiation, the forehead of the body carries a red adhesive disk. If the corpse is infectious, it must also be clearly marked to signify this. The Mortuary book must contain the names of those who conduct the autopsy and of those who are present to observe, as well as the names of persons who remove bodies from the building. Records must be kept of organs removed also. When a body arrives, it is weighed and measured. The following visual inspection seeks to discover abnormalities which might reveal the secrets of death. The police, the GP and relatives are all sources of information from which a history for an uncertified case is built up. According to Prior, the contemporary pathologist is forever forced to look beyond the livid body within the mortuary walls, into the social, occupational and political world in which the deceased once lived, in order to elaborate causation.

Prior's study of the mortuary therefore sees its role in a much wider sense than just a building in which bodies are stored or from which they are moved elsewhere by the funeral service. It is a place where the investigative powers of the state and the explanatory principles of scientific medicine interact to 'police' the dead, not so much in matters of security as in the preservation of 'social health'. In this setting, the forensic pathologist provides the clinical gaze and the inquisitive state bureaucracy the investigative rights over the corpse, to unveil any possible dangers to public or private welfare. Prior looked at the Belfast inquests of 1982 to support his case and found in the Coroner's Summary Statements (representing 50% of all inquests) references to a wide range of personal details, specifying not only homicides and deaths from road accidents, but also a mention of drinking and eating habits, physical living arrangements, previous illnesses, family relationships, emotional states, sleeping habits, even political beliefs and leisure interests. All this, apart from the routine data of marital status, occupation, age, place of residence, social class and place of death.

THE PATHOLOGIST NO LONGER THE SOLE ARBITER OF CAUSE (OF DEATH)

The pathologist's concern is with damage to the body at the basic level because there has been damage to groups of cells. Pathology is the study of what goes wrong and why. Briefly, the main causes of damage occur by means which are: microbiological (bacteria, viruses, fungi); chemical (poisons, drugs, toxic gases); physical (burns, cold, irradiation); nutritional (lack of vitamins, proteins, trace elements); hypoxic (lack of oxygen through reduced blood supply); immunological (where the body reacts against itself, usually producing antibodies); and genetic (where the body has an inbuilt failure to develop normally to perhaps produce the wrong types of substances - Haemophilia, for example, where no clotting factor is produced to stop a body from bleeding). Dr. Lindley (1988) stated in a lecture that one person in five dies in a mysterious way. It is likely that a post-mortem will follow. The Coroner will be involved if a doctor has not seen the deceased or does not know the cause of death; this applies to any death which is unnatural, occurred from an industrial disease, during an operation or under anesthesia. These precise concerns of pathology, including the forensic elements, needed to be established before proceeding to probe Prior's propositions. So, a person is either dead or not dead, medically speaking. If the person is dead, there will have been a cessation of perspiration, absence of heart sounds, loss of corneal reflex, fragmentation of blood and columns in the retinal vessels (leaving aside the complications of brain death and transplants, and the abortion debate). However, what Prior suggests is that the findings of modern pathology have to be 'meshed into a set of broader social, moral and political concerns before adequate causal accounts of pathological states can be constructed.' Hence, to discover the cause of death is not just the concern of mortuary pathology but has also to do with political and legal agencies of the modern state in which the mortuary operates. Can cause really be located outside the body in a way in which deaths from natural causes are not? It is only in cases of unnatural death that pathology is forced to spell out precisely its aetiological logic, argues Prior. His case is briefly put below.

A mortuary will store many cadavers that are merely in transit for the funeral services to take charge. For other cases, the search for the causes of human mortality is located in two dissections; the physical of flesh and bone, but also the one that precedes it, which is the theoretical one. Pathology, making use of visual observation, looks for abnormalities in the body. But not all abnormalities are attended by disease. Pathology is dominated also by the concept of the normal evident in a mortuary, although the purpose of dissection is to discover the abnormal in the anatomy. Normality can be measured and Prior gives us the weights of a liver, brain, heart, even testicles. If therefore the abnormal/pathological is only a quantitative variation on the normal/physiological, then the mortuary can release all the secrets of organic degeneration. Whatever is then external to the corpse in the outside world would be of no concern. If, however, the pathological is something qualitatively different from the physiological, it is another type of 'normal' entirely and must be measured in the context of the complete and concrete individual, and not just with organs and functions.

Prior makes the claim that the causes for the pathological condition cannot be obtained from the body alone and that pathology is forced to look outside the human frame for causal factors, given such predisposing matters as racial or geographical factors, age, nutrition, social and cultural influences. If this reasoning is accepted, the power of the pathologist to pronounce authoritatively on cause is severely curbed and likely to undermine status and prestige in the medico-legal world. Prior offers us a case illustration in support of his conclusion. The deceased was a 91 year old woman living alone, very independent and mentally alert (refusing offers of residential accommodation, meals-on-wheels and day centre attendance). Some home help was available and a neighbour visited her regularly, as did the local social services supervisor. A niece helped with the shopping. Ample food and heating was available but the woman insisted on heating only the room she was using. One day the home help found the deceased lying unconscious on the cold kitchen floor. She died some days later in the hospital. The medical causes of acute renal failure and hypothermia were regarded as an unsatisfactory explanation of death by the Coroner and the pathologist was also not satisfied. In general, a Coroner would be interested in moral blame as well as cause. In this case he has focused on personality traits, material conditions, personal relationships and means of subsistence (additional to the somatic elements) in his attempt to explain the medical conditions. Given that the medical and the social (through medico-legal surveillance) are both events separated in the mortuary, Prior feels that a distinction between cause and verdict or between cause and mode of death simply does not hold, and that the vocabulary of causation must be so elaborated as to include the social factors outside the mortuary as a significant part in the chain which led up to the death in question.

SELECTIVITY IN CORPSE DISSECTION

According to Knight,(1980) it was the poor and the criminals who, during the early part of the 19th Century, ended up under the pathologists' scalpels, if their bodies were unclaimed, in the hope that organic and possibly also the social causes of death might be located. With the gradual extension of medical audits, the autopsy became the weapon in the analysis of all forms of disease and bodily disorder. It is the claim of criminologists that such investigative resources are frequently so structured as to favour social and political interests, which would seem to be true for pathology also, although specified with such precision as to give all of us a chance (but according to Prior, not necessarily an equal chance) to end up on the mortuary slab. Prior's Belfast investigation in 1982 informs us that of the 900 cadavers sent to the city mortuary for storage or dissection, some 680 were Coroner cases. His 25% survey of these clients, plus a 10% sample of all Belfast deaths in 1981, were the tools he used to locate the 'social characteristics of those who slide across the mortuary table' to discover an emergent pattern. It is useful here to restate forensic pathology's concern, which is with unnatural as well as with suspicious, sudden or puzzling deaths. What meets this definition depends on the defined circumstances of each case, upon which are superimposed certain informal social norms such as: the proper age to die, the proper place to be found dead, or indeed the proper manner of dying. The daily routine may, therefore, evidence some selectivity as is qualitatively illustrated in the works of Sudnow (1967) and Glaser & Strauss (1965), when these authors suggest that medical resources devoted to the dying tend to be distributed according to their perceived social status or estimated social value. This, Prior explains, is quite consistent with his Coroner data in the Belfast study of 1985.

EROSION OR ENHANCEMENT?
THE CORONER'S FUNCTION FACING BOTH WAYS

The eroding trend beginning as early as 1926 gained momentum with the Criminal Law Act, 1977 which (in the words of Mason, 1983) emasculated the Coroner's Office by removing from his (sic) jurisdiction cases of murder, manslaughter, infanticide or killing by reckless driving. His powers to recommend safeguards against recurrence of actions prejudicial to the public interest were also curtailed. An earlier Government Report (HMSO, 1971) on Death Certification and Coroners was critical about his role in the detection of homicides and said that the prime task of the Coroner today is to furnish the accurate 'medical' causes of death to the Registrar General. Mason suggests that medico-legal autopsies could well be cleared by the Coroner to be handled by teams of clinicians and pathologists in an integrated co-operative effort and thereby restore manifest sudden 'natural' death cases to academic departments of pathology, where he thinks they properly belong. His suggestion excludes research-oriented autopsies. Mant (1986) likewise agrees that natural death cases should be a part of the routine duties and indeed the main function of the National Health Service pathologists and not be dealt with by the Coroner.

Prior's interpretation, however, could be understood as supporting an enhancement of the Coroner's role. The evidence he gathered from the World Health Organisation (W.H.O.), Belfast and Census statistics led him to conclude that Coroners appear to focus their investigative resources on particular segments of the population and possess the power to distribute their verdicts (at least partly so) in accordance with socio-political judgments. Thus, men's deaths are more likely to be investigated and their death regarded as 'unnatural' than that of women.

The same is true of middle-class as against working-class; married as against unmarried, widowed or single status; and the economically active as against the inactive. One investigative resource is the power of autopsy. Not all cadavers in the mortuary are selected for autopsy, although all are processed by the Coroner and have in common that a G.P. or hospital doctor could not certify death. But over and above that, non-clinical factors also play a part in the crucial decision whether or not an autopsy is performed.

Age is found to correlate strongly with autopsy, with the under-sixties being far more selected than the economically inactive age groups, as are also infants and children. As to gender, men in the higher age groups are more often autopsied than women. The evidence confirms by and large the expending of extra resources on the 'socially valued'. One must infer from Prior's data that the more cautious, suspicious, or socially-minded Coroner refers more cadavers for autopsy. Corpse discrimination also affects the forensic pathologist, who reserves his scalpel as an investigating instrument for distinct and specific segments of the population. But the selection is in the hands of the Coroner, which in the view of more than one writer on the future of forensic medicine (Mason, 1983, Mant, 1986) is merely maintaining an expensive tradition. What does the present day inquest do, Mant asks, except provide copy for the local press and rubber-stamp investigations in cases of public interest which have already been carried out by specialised investigators as, for instance, in cases of aircraft or train accidents?

There is a distinction between a natural/unnatural death; normal/abnormal death; sudden and suspicious death; so that at some stage within the mechanisms of apportioning pathology work, the Coroner will become involved. As far as forensic pathology is concerned, Prior's view is that the practitioners cannot distance themselves from the convergence of the medical and legal interest with the social residing in the corpse. He makes the point that medical advances continue to focus on new clinical specialisms which make such earlier and vague diagnostic specifications as 'immaturity' in infants or 'cardiac debility' and 'myocardial failure' in adults as cause of death no longer acceptable. His evidence has suggested that such factors as age, gender, occupation and marital status, are widely utilised to signify potential pathological states, so that the social cannot be divorced from the clinical in the selection of cases for autopsy, and so also in its search for the origins of death by the forensic pathologist.

Some views of practising forensic pathologists I have gathered ran counter to Prior's view. To begin with, the retardation in the development of forensic medicine attributed by Camps (1968) to the Spilsbury tradition of individualism, has occurred alongside the scientific advances in this field. As explained by Cameron (1980) later, there is an underlying financial philosophy which exemplifies this state by a Coroner paying autopsy fees only to establish cause of death and not to do investigations of interest. The latter might well allude to the attending social circumstances leading to cause. Dr. Hunt (1989) points out that the Coroners' system in this country existed before the Norman Conquest and if William could not get rid of it, what chance do we stand?   The background information required about the dead in England has not that much changed during the last thousand years and is still influenced among other historical incidents by the Norman Murder Tax. Dr. Hunt, who is a Histopathologist, thinks that Dr. Prior's idea of the pathologist in the U.K. is a false one. There is no influence upon him by the State. He is entirely an agent of the Coroner and the Coroner is only partly an arm of the State. Dr. Hunt disagrees with Dr. Prior also on other matters. For example, on the proposition that the 'deaths of men are regarded as unnatural more often than that of women', this is not so much a socio-political phenomenon as the simple fact that more men die an unnatural death than do women.   He would accept that there is a somewhat decreased percentage incidence of reporting of natural deaths to the Coroner in patients from Socio-economic Group 1, but this is explained (partly, at least) by the fact that GPs are more likely to visit patients in that group, and to feel able to sign death certificates.

Notwithstanding these reservations, we are still left with the one big question that Prior poses: '.....death cannot be investigated in terms of the body alone.....' (1987:357), which demands further discussion.

THE VULNERABILITY OF A CORONER'S PATHOLOGIST

If Prior's pronouncement that 'the cadaver.....is at once a solution to a riddle and an obstacle to knowledge' (op.cit., p 360), is accepted, the implication is that a Coroner's Jury, for example, would be much wiser giving their verdict on the deceased if they had known his/her peculiarities and life-style.   It is not unreasonable to assume such information would help the forensic pathologist in arriving at an opinion as to cause which is more than just 'obvious'. That view is not, however, shared by all forensic pathologists in the investigation of cause of death. A well-known (but unnamed) such doctor of former years is quoted as having claimed that autopsies should be performed 'blind', so that pre-knowledge could not bias his eventual conclusion. Given that a verdict on cause can be tested by cross-examination in Court, the position of the medical witness can take on precarious dimensions (Leadbeatter and Knight, 1987). The implications of the slings and arrows of expert evidence and the dangers to professional reputations, if miscarriage of justice results, will be considered in a later section of this chapter. For now, the question posed by Leadbeatter and Knight - 'how much in a medico-legal autopsy the pathologist's knowledge of the antecedent circumstances should influence him in offering a cause of death' - will be of prime concern.

It is the view of these authors that whereas case history may be a dominant factor in clinical medicine in arriving at a diagnosis, but that in forensic pathology the situation is much more complex because (a) the history does not come directly from the deceased; (b) the circumstances of death may be such as to affect the reliability and veracity of the witnesses; and (c) the investigation may be inadequate and yield a history which, although not inaccurate, is significantly incomplete. These doctors consider such knowledge of prime importance in determining the conduct of an autopsy. They are against a 'blind' examination on the grounds that it would have to cover all possible eventualities and, moreover, require prohibitively expensive and time-consuming techniques, embracing the need for a 'blanket' investigation of each autopsy to include full toxicology, microbiology, virology, radiology and such. Economic restraint, and the desperate shortage of forensic pathologists, would make such a policy not only impracticable but also impossible. At the same time, the authors are alive to the obvious dangers in simply omitting parts of an investigation by reliance on inadequate histories. They cite the experience of two recent instances where autopsy findings of natural disease were consistent with history, but where belated information about self-poisoning forced an urgent second autopsy before the bodies were taken from the mortuary.

If, say, multiple diseases are found in an autopsied body, knowing the history is helpful in assessing what might have been the likely cause of death. The situation is just as problematic when only one disease is found. In death due to a hepatic failure from cirrhosis of the liver, for example, without the availability of an ante-mortem biopsy and postmortem histology (tissue structure) revealing only mixed-nodular cirrhosis without any evidence of the aetiology, a little social background information can go a long way. In one case, the mortuary technician's wife's brother owned the local liquor store and the technician informed the pathologist that the deceased had been his brother-in-law's principal customer. Is the case of death now to be reported as 'cirrhosis of liver, aetiology unknown', or is it to be 'alcoholic cirrhosis', ask the authors? Were there to be an ante-biopsy available and reported on as 'alcoholic hepatitis', the situation would be a different one if the pathologist's biopsy review could exclude perhexiline maleate (cardiac variation control) from the patient's pharmacopoeia (accepted drug standards).

Quite often an autopsy reveals the second of the two alternatives - findings or no findings. Take the case of a patient admitted to hospital in wintertime with a rectal temperature of 26c who dies two days later. At autopsy, there were signs of hypothermia, yet the clinical records could not be disputed. Similar deaths are known also to arise from epilepsy and asthma, where there may be a clear history but no relevant autopsy findings. The question the authors now ask is whether it is valid to use history almost exclusively in arriving at an opinion as to cause of death, in contrast to signing out all such cases as 'unascertained'. To further illustrate the ramifications of this question, these doctors provide interesting examples associated with cot deaths. Usually, the 'Sudden Infant Death Syndrome' (known as SIDS) reveals no lesions sufficient to account for death. In former years, such deaths were speculatively reported from 'suffocation' to 'capillary bronchiolitis' (inflamed lung and breathing affected), none of which was true in the majority of cases. Thus, in cot deaths, the purists would simply certify them as 'unascertained', although this often engendered undesirable social repercussions. To so label many thousands of such cases today is unacceptable, especially as SIDS now has international recognition as the most common cause of post-perinatal mortality, although the designation SIDS is really a diagnosis of exclusion, based on a typical history and absence of positive autopsy findings. It appears that a pathologist has to (seemingly with the legitimate connivance of the Coroner) use hearsay knowledge of the circumstances to arrive at a speculative, though prima facie reasonable cause of death. Now with autopsy findings of SIDS being nil and autopsy findings in most infant suffocations also nil, the pathologist is faced with the obvious dilemma of how to tell the difference. The question here posed is whether he should even attempt to do this or leave judgement in the hands of the law. Leadbeatter and Knight (1987) report a recent case where multiple sudden infant deaths occurred in the same family. Whilst the autopsy findings were consistently negative, the repetitive circumstances persuaded the pathologist that the latest death was due to suffocation. Lengthy legal proceedings followed because the pathologist used his knowledge of the circumstances, rather than 'pathological lesions', to form an opinion as to the cause of death. This has been challenged on the basis of a different interpretation of the circumstances.

THE PATHOLOGIST - A CATCH 22 SITUATION?

By and large, pathologists like to adhere in the presentation of their autopsy reports to the format prescribed by the World Health Organisation in its rule book on 'Medical Certification of Cause of Death'. This WHO (1978) booklet directs doctors concerned 'in the case of accident, poisoning or violence, to enter a brief description of the external cause on the line immediately below the description of the type of injury or poisoning'. On another page, even more specific directions are given as for example in relation to poisoning, where the doctor is required to state on the certificate whether this was '.....accidental, suicidal or homicidal'. The authors say that in the instances of some Coroners they have encountered, such autopsy reports would very likely be seen as prejudicial to the legal category of death and possibly even to matters of culpability. Indeed, recent changes in coroners' legislation (Coroners Act, 1980) puts the legality of this into question. There are at present still great variations in the practices different coroners and pathologists adopt, as there are also between an individual coroner and the pathologist at different times and in different circumstances. Moreover, the public are not averse to challenging contentious inquests, which for the pathologist means utmost care in deciding and recording the opinions given. These writers have also recognised the major dilemma for a pathologist to define the threshold below which he or she is not prepared to pronounce cause on the basis of circumstantial hearsay evidence if anatomic findings are not also available. The pathologist could take the road of erring on the side of caution and use the term 'unascertained' as the cot death example has shown. But if there is too rigid an adherence to the stance that only visual evidence can be used in assisting the legal authorities, there is the risk of (say the authors) accusations of 'abdicating his (sic) responsibilities and even being obstructive'.

A good illustration is the case of a body brought to autopsy with a history furnished by the police. The man fell from a low factory roof whilst doing the work of window cleaning. The autopsy clearly demonstrates severe head injuries and the pathologist uses the format of the WHO on cause of death when writing his report. If he is (a) purely anatomic, he will write 'fractured skull and lacerations of brain'. If he opts for being more circumstantial, he would add (b) fall from a height; and if he wished to be much more precise, he would replace the words in (b) by 'fall from a factory roof'. The pathologist cannot tell from the examination alone how the man came by his injuries. They might well appear classically pathological of a fall from a height, but not only are injuries often not as specific, also the autopsy alone can never reveal to the pathologist that the victim fell from the roof of a factory. Leadbeatter & Knight (1987) make it very clear that some Coroners in England and Wales request their pathologists to use the more precise version of the WHO in their autopsy reports whilst others specifically forbid it and hold that 'the sole function of the pathologist is to discover the anatomic cause of death, and to leave a decision as to the means by which that cause came to operate to the legal authority charged with categorising and disposing of the case'. The path to be trodden seems to be narrow and tortuous between 'unwarranted speculation' on the one hand and 'obstinate caution' on the other. Is history always reliable as a signpost along this path? Additional stages in the chain of an investigation may bring information to light for a history to be changed. Should then a pathologist change an opinion already given? In any event, original or subsequently changed circumstances are capable of interpretation in several ways. Why then (ask the authors) should a possibly inaccurate or incomplete history dictate the view that the pathologist chooses to give?

Another example is given to illustrate that all circumstances are capable of more than one interpretation. Taking the death of an old person, there is nothing in the pathological evidence to exclude plastic-bag asphyxia, even though sufficient natural disease is present to account for death. The pathologist in this case realistically assumes the absence of circumstances to indicate that breathing was obstructed by a plastic bag over the deceased's head if there is no reasonable suspicion and see the cause as, say, a 'coronary artery disease'. In the view of the authors, this is not 'abdication of responsibility' but native prudence to be cautious when offering an opinion in cases where the legal process obviously indicates such opinion to be based on hearsay evidence. A pathologist is not precluded from an identification of the various possibilities in his report under a heading of 'differential diagnosis'; but, what should be avoided in the absence of objective pathological evidence, is to give any one of the possibilities a seal of approval by specifying it as a definite cause of death. The authors prefer the ultimate decision and responsibility to be in the hands of the appropriate investigating authority, which in England and Wales is the Coroner, and the duty of the pathologist and clinicians to be merely advisory to that authority, albeit as fully and as accurately as possible. It therefore follows (in these authors' opinion) that the pathologist should base his or her conclusions of the cause of death on the pathological findings, with the history serving only to show up a need for special investigation.

Thus, dilemmas abound for the forensic pathologist in cases of sudden or unexpected death. He or she may have to satisfy relatives, the police, coroner, registrar, often the Courts and may even have to account for a discrepancy between a clinical and autopsy cause of death. This doctor has, moreover, to ponder upon the social circumstances entering into the deliberations, which causes these authors to ask: 'In a Coroner system as it operates at present, should the pathologist stick his (sic) neck out and in these litigious days risk having his head chopped off?'. One typical case, where knowledge of the social circumstances leading to an extinction of life would be of no help to the pathologist occurred where a man of 36 and a girl of 14 had died together by drinking a mixture of cyanide and sulphuric acid. The jury at the inquest returned a verdict that the man killed himself but that the girl had been unlawfully killed. A pathologist would not, of course, be able to say whether she died of her own free will or not (The Times 11.4.1984). Were this country to operate a medical examiner system as in some parts of the United States, a so-called 'pathologist-coroner' would combine the various parts of an investigation and in the use of both autopsy findings and antecedents reach a decision without an inquest. Leadbeatter and Knight recommend that the best available evidence be used to base an opinion on and then the pathologist, if the need arises, should be prepared to defend it in the legal arena. They are not satisfied with some of the instructions on death certification in the WHO booklet as far as coroners' pathologists are concerned and advise a revision in the next edition.

The determination of 'cause of death' is riddled with complexities. The forensic pathologist's autonomy in giving a verdict has obvious limits and stress is not confined to handling the remains of a body whose anatomy he or she shares; disputed findings by colleagues and the Courts may often arouse media attention to taint professional reputations and the cycle may end with the stigma of incompetence and career destruction. The Clift case, which started with the body of a woman found in a wood and ended some nine years later with the retirement of the pathologist 'in the public interests', rocked the British forensic science establishment to its foundations. Such new principles as this important case established will be further examined in Chapter 6.

CHAPTER 4

THE EMERGENCE OF LEGAL MEDICINE - FROM 19TH CENTURY CORPSE EXAMINERS TO CHAIRS IN UNIVERSITIES

This profession faces today some key problems, serious enough to affect its scientific credibility, its recruitment and the public image of forensic pathology itself. And yet, the role played by these practitioners has never been exposed to systematic sociological research as could (and it is my belief would) illuminate its position and clear the path towards a better understanding of its current difficulties. Forensic science as a regular practical discipline is not yet a hundred years old, although in its empirical form it has existed for many centuries. Hence the downgrading tendencies, of which the disposal of the 'corpse examiner' in the late 19th Century Europe is an example, must be placed into an earlier historical context to show how certain occupational blemishes emerged.

Prior to the 16th Century, there was no separate specialty of legal medicine, no practitioners or medicologists, no writings on the subject and only spasmodic influences of the law on medicine. The first known law codes in the earliest annals and sacred books of primitive peoples provide evidence for this. In the latter years of the last Century records became more frequent and study more intense, until at last a separate discipline arose whose origin and development through the centuries was capable of being studied in a more systematic fashion in different countries. From the earliest times, medicine and law were first united by the bonds of religion, superstition and magic. The functions of the physician and jurist were combined in the priest as an intermediary between God and man, to promulgate God-given law and judging breaches of that law. Disease and death were seen as divine punishment for the non-observing, or caused by magic or evil spirits. But the priest also functioned as physician and witch doctor, so that direct treatment (through knowledge of toxic plants), supplemented by sacrifice and prayer, gave him considerable power. (Camps, 1968). From what we know of many countries, there was ignorance, apathy, parsimony and conflicting interest which caused reverses to progress in the forensic field, but many of these were local or temporary and advancement seemed to continue. Under the old law codes in Babylon a physician causing death in error could have his hands cut off; in Persia criminal abortions were heavily punished;   Greece had no autopsies because dead bodies were sacred;   early Rome provided that the bodies of dying women in confinement should be opened to try to save the child's life;   in India the diseased were not permitted to be witnesses in court;   and in Egypt it was the priest who pronounced on the cause of death. From the late 16th Century onwards, there was to be found a mass of literature on deaths from wounds, abortion, infanticide, deaths by lightning, hanging, drowning, feigned diseases, and the differentiation between ante- and postmortem wounds. Poisons by carbon monoxide and by corrosives were also written about. Many model reports became available and ethical standards were then seen as high. The subject itself was already recognised as a separate entity in medicine. (Mant, 1984). One might add to this outline that the 17th and 18th Centuries were periods of rapid advance across Europe and in other parts of the world, as evidenced by the mass of publications and the establishment of Chairs in Universities. It was also in continental Europe where by the 19th Century the era of modern legal medicine commenced, although individual men of letters everywhere (and not least in Scotland) had kept in close touch with the centre of learning there. Whilst the detailed landmarks of the developing forensic sciences in Asia, the Middle East, Europe and America have had to be omitted, a discussion of how the scalpel fell upon forensic pathology in this country is highly topical for this research. In the year 1312 Italy had its first public dissection and experienced prejudices against such practices for the next 200 years and people like Fidelis of Palermo and Zacchias of Rome produced case notes on drowning, cardiac deaths, knife cuts, bullet wounds, asphyxiation, and infanticide, and so made their mark. Bonet in Geneva performed 3000 autopsies and by the 16th Century managed with the publication of his work to vanquish the distaste felt for post-mortems at this time. Both the Dane, Batholinus, and Schreyer from Bratislava experimented on the content of air in the lungs of a child to determine whether it was born alive or as a corpse. Primitive courses in forensic medicine were started by Bohn at Leipzig University in 1704, thereby bestowing academic respectability upon a previously despised science. Major universities in Prague and Vienna followed. The French physician Fodore, a former surgeon in Napoleon's armies in publishing in 1908 the 'Code Napoleon' put the administrative flesh on his theories and established the occupation of 'Medical Examiner' as a vital public service, rather than a secret ghoulish ritual, as perceived before. That, in a nutshell was the state of play in Europe.

LEGAL MEDICINE IN GREAT BRITAIN

The teaching of medical jurisprudence in British universities lagged somewhat behind the European continent. The first chair in the UK was not established until 1807, when Andrew Duncan was appointed Professor of Medical Jurisprudence and Medical Police at Edinburgh University. Prior to this, Samuel Farr wrote the first systematic book on jurisprudence in English, of which the later edition in 1815 included a chapter on the 'Observation of Signs of Murder in the Case of Bastard Children'. Duncan, like his fellow surgeons, was hampered by the restrictive laws on the use of bodies for dissection. These were also the main cause leading to the 'body snatching' or 'resurrection' practice as it was called. Burke and Hare were two of those who murdered victims for sale to the Edinburgh Anatomy School. When Duncan left, the main occupant of the chair became Sir Robert Christison at the young age of 24, who later enjoyed international fame and took part in the Burke and Hare trial. His 'Treatise on Poisons' remained for long the best work in English on the subject. Professor Traill next occupied the chair for thirty years and made the subject compulsory for medical students long before the Medical Act of 1858 required it for all medical schools. At that time, a Coroner in England still had no power to pay for medical evidence at inquests and doubt existed also whether he had power to order a postmortem examination. Whilst more chairs were established in Scotland (such as at Glasgow and Aberdeen), the development of legal medicine in England was less satisfactory although there is evidence of important books and outstanding scholars. It was the organisation and general recognition of the subject which still left a lot to be desired.

The Smethhurst case in 1859 (Smyth, 1980) did little to help the subject to keep abreast with the advances in Europe. This Doctor was charged with poisoning Isabella Banks. A leading toxicologist examined the tissues of the body and discovered traces of arsenic in them. At the trial to follow the magistrate's hearing it emerged that the arsenic had come from faulty testing equipment. There were also wrangles in Court between the toxicologist and two other forensic experts. When Dr. Smethhurst was still convicted, there were protests in the Lancet and the Times publicly denigrated the evidence from toxicology. The Home Secretary then referred the case to independent specialists and in the end Dr. Smethhurst was acquitted. The Dublin Medical Journal accused the toxicologist of having brought disrepute upon this branch of the profession that it would take many years to overcome. That prediction in fact came true until toxicological and pathological evidence helped to convict

Crippen 40 years later, when 'orthodox' medical views and the British press felt able to accord some recognition to this branch of science. This case helped to restore some degree of public confidence and trust through three brilliant scientists at St. Mary's Hospital in London. These three, to be later joined by a young medical student (Bernard Spilsbury who was to gain worldwide fame), encouraged the latter's enthusiasm for and interest in toxicology and histology. Spilsbury never wrote the book he promised from his copious case notes, but it was he and one of the three (Dr. Pepper) who destroyed the Crippen defences. He was typical of the charismatic individuals rather than forensic medicine as such to make their mark, and his reputation grew to such an extent that his appearance for the prosecution was said to be able to sway a case. One of Spilsbury's main contributions was the encouragement of offshoots to his craft - forensic physics and chemistry. Another was the introduction of the 'murder bag', containing all the essentials needed when called out. The idea came to him when at one case he was horrified to see a local police superintendent handling the dreadful remains with his bare hands. The murder bag was subsequently adopted by police forces all over the world. No one knows whether it was occupational stress that caused Spilsbury to gas himself in his laboratory at University College London in 1947, his headquarters at the time.

If Spilsbury made his mark in the medico-legal field, another man to achieve equal fame for his pioneering efforts in forensic medicine following his medical studies in Edinburgh, was the New Zealander, Sidney Alfred Smith. A great admirer of Sherlock Holmes, he adopted as his dicta of successful detection the 'power to observe and deduct' and the 'possession of a wide range of precise knowledge'. Smith was something of a social scientist because, in addition to amassing medical knowledge of a wide range, he was also interested in the way people dressed, their different cultural eating habits, the attitudes and postures of frightened as against angry attackers, and the mode of defence their victims adopted. Such extended interests would seem to be missing from the approaches of the latter-day pathologists, (see Chapter 6). By the early 1920s, Dr. Smith became medico-legal adviser to the Egyptian Government, founded the Forensic Department at the University of Cairo and became the first professor there. The high incidence of crime in the country provided him with scope to experiment and he soon acquired expertise in ballistics and toxicology, building his own special microscope when he could not obtain one from America. Eventually the association with Edinburgh University was resumed and Professor Smith turned it into one of the leading centres of the world for the study of forensic science. His textbook, published in

1928, ran into many editions and he attracted students world-wide by his witty seminars. Widely mourned when he died in 1969 as Emeritus Professor and Rector of the University he is said to have made this branch of medical science a respectable discipline. (Smyth, p.29).

As can be seen from this brief history, a small number of individuals helped to carve the reputation of British forensic medicine up to the second world war. Another such personality was Professor John Glaister of Glasgow University who made his mark around the same time as Sidney Smith, this mainly by writing authoritatively on the subjects of Medical Jurisprudence and Toxicology. This text, first published in 1902, ran into many revised editions and was so highly regarded that it has today become the 'Bible' for criminal pathologists in Britain, Australia and America. Glaister was not merely a theoretician, as was shown by his complex reconstruction in 1935 of the Buck Ruxton case, with which he and a colleague were closely involved. A concisely presented illustration of the case will demonstrate how forensic pathologists work. The two doctors had the grisly task of piecing together the seventy human remains found in a gully off the Edinburgh-Moffat road. The killer had gone to enormous lengths to avoid discovery by cutting strips of fatty tissue and flesh off the body, removing eyes and lips, and scattering the portions over a wide area. It was established that there were, in fact, two murder victims and that they were women. Some novel methods were used in the forensic investigation: including superimposing a picture of one of the victims over the skull to assess the fit; making flexi-castes from the two left feet found in a reasonable state of preservation among the remains and measuring the fit in the shoes of the murdered woman; examining the drains in the suspect's house to obtain blood tissues which matched those of the corpses; and obtaining dermal prints from hands already badly decomposed, a procedure never adopted before. (Smyth, pp. 30-32).

This case showed also how forensic science can be advanced by the enlistment of other specialists. Physicists and other experts helped with a microscopic examination of parts of the cotton sheets to trace the loom in the suspect's house. In the end, the evidence was so conclusive that Dr. Buck Ruxton (formerly Bukhtyar Hakin) was convicted and in 1936 hanged for the murder of Mrs. Ruxton his wife, and Mary Rogerson her nursemaid. One of the major reasons why so much importance attached to the case was the employment of team work in the investigation. It provided an impetus for the development of highly specialised professional disciplines in scientific criminology, which now include Immunology and Serology (the study of blood, urine, saliva and sperm);

Odontology (the study of teeth as a most durable part of the body); Ballistics, a field in which medical examiners are closely involved; Toxicology and Chemistry which have long been important areas in the history of this science (see for example Orfila who in 1787 catalogued poisons and their effects); and in more recent times, Psychiatry, where mentally unbalanced or psychotic cases are involved. At an experimental stage still is the exciting new specialism of Voiceprinting, sometimes known as 'Articulators', which brings electronic engineering into crime detection. (Smyth, pp. 32-33).

PROBLEMS WITH RECOGNITION AND RESEARCH

The take-off of legal medicine was more pronounced in Scotland than in England, although excellent books and outstanding scholars existed. Of the thirty-seven medical schools providing instruction in the bigger cities of the United Kingdom by the mid-19th Century when the subject was obligatory, status and recognition vanished in later years when these established chairs lapsed. Now, there are only five personal Chairs of which three are at the University of London and the others at Leeds and Sheffield. In Scotland, the Chair in Aberdeen has lapsed but the Regius Chairs in Edinburgh and Glasgow still exist. According to Cameron (1980), prior to the Second World War few if any thought of forensic medicine as an academic domain and painfully little research came from those who specialised in, or had any experience of, the subject. Far from enjoying the respect and help it needed from its elders in academic pathology, the specialty was despised by them for its divorce from the University Schools (Simpson, 1963). Too many untrained specialists emerged as a result of innumerable autopsies, providing a vivid contrast to the charismatic personalities like Spilsbury and Smith, ably supported later by such well-known names as Simpson, Camps, Teare, Glaister and Polson. A Medico-Legal Society was not formed until 1903, which was the only learned society devoted to the subject. Untrained practitioners in Coroners' and police pathology enlisted advice and help only when required for examples in cases of poisoning, which demanded more precise analysis. Similarly serology and stain analysis, what little there was, rarely challenged existing knowledge, or practices, in pathology.

Thus, until the post-war years, the reputation of 'English' forensic medicine rested largely in the hands of one or two highly reputed individuals. Thereafter, however, a change occurred. Legal medicine received the recognition it had lacked before. After 1950, the British

Association in Forensic Medicine (BAFM) was founded and the Forensic Science Society (FSS) saw the light of day. The British Academy of Forensic Sciences (BAFS) also came into being. There was, at last, a realization that the investigation of medico-legal cases frequently requires collaboration with specialists in other disciplines. The media has always seen to it that sensational cases were brought to the attention of the general public. In this way, the average citizen can relate reality to fictional television. Notwithstanding these developments, it is feared that academic forensic medicine has gone steadily downhill until there is now a danger (according to same opinions conveyed also in my data) of its extinction. Already some university departments have been made sub-departments and others abolished (as explained to me in an interview with Professor Cameron, May, 1989). The present situation was predicted by the late Professor Glaister as early as 1951, when he addressed members of the BAFM, during which he talked of the difficulties which would arise from the exclusion of forensic medicine as a constituent of the then newly-formed state medical service in 1948, either unintentionally or by design, and the absence of any specialists practising the subject. In his presidential address to the BAFS in 1980, Professor Cameron made it clear that not all the blame could be attached to the universities for this wane in academic legal medicine. Their job is to teach undergraduates the essentials of forensic medicine and they could claim, with considerable justification, that the provision of forensic medicine for the community is not their concern, particularly so when money is short and the new medical specialties (such as mentioned earlier) are clamouring for recognition and upgrading.(Cameron, 1980) In most universities forensic medicine is virtually self-supporting, thus forming, in the view of Knight (1967), the only basis for its toleration.

A DIAGNOSIS OF THE PRESENT CRISIS

A review of courses in medical jurisprudence in 1951 revealed a great variation in the length of time devoted to this subject, taken by Cameron as the practical reflection of particular attitudes held by some of the bodies in question. For example, the Goodenough Report in 1944 of the Inter-departmental Committee on Medical Schools (HMSO, 1944) offered only the brief comment that instruction to students in some medical schools on forensic medicine seemed excessive, having regard to the needs of general practice. On the other hand, the General Medical Council (in connection with the Goodenough Committee's Report) held that since every GP was liable to be called upon at short notice notice to deal with questions within the realm of forensic medicine, it was imperative that due weight should continue to be attached to this subject in the curriculum. A later report (the Todd Report on Medical Education in 1968) (HMSO, 1968) made no reference to forensic medicine at all. At the very least, these are some indicators of an ambivalent approach towards this discipline.

Cameron gave voice also to the anxiety that the lack of availability and quality of medico-legal experts caused, as these properly trained experts were rapidly disappearing from the scene, together with prospects for postgraduate training. This, in the opinion of Cameron (1973), is at least partly due to the accent placed on pathology rather than on medicine, because the modern medico-legist should be more concerned with the broader aspects of legal medicine than just the limited field of morbid anatomy. Given an approximate 56 million people in the UK (inclusive of IoM and Channel Islands) in an area of some 95,000 square miles, there were, at the time of Cameron's address to the Academy in 1980, barely 50 full-time 'professional' forensic pathologists in total, that is, just one medico-legal expert per some 1,120,000 persons, or approximately one such expert per 2,000 square miles. This small number of doctors regularly carries out thousands of investigations into homicides or possible criminal cases for Coroners and Fiscals in the entire UK, making, indeed, autopsy a 'dying art'.

Francis Camps, seeking in 1968 to explain this state of affairs, attributed the cause to the 'Spilsbury tradition of individualism'. Although no longer seen as the norm today, this position may possibly have been instrumental in producing some outstanding personalities, even if it has done little to encourage suitable prospects for the specialty and its practitioners. In the view of Cameron, it may also be responsible for a general lagging behind of forensic medicine relative to advances in the field of forensic science, in part at least demonstrated by the attitude of coroners to pay solely for determining cause at autopsy, thereby ignoring wider circumstantial or social concerns that may have contributed to the death in question. Presumably the latter includes the kind of extra-cadaver associations of a social nature that Prior had in mind. This cash-nexus philosophy might well explain the reason for the substitution of a cause of death which is 'obvious', for the cause of death which is 'correct'. Suspicion is the first line of detection in England and Wales under the present Coroners' system where murder is concerned, as is also the need to recognise death which is unnatural (Johnson, 1969). When sudden or unexpected death occurs, a medical practitioner is virtually always required to pronounce that life is 'extinct'. Hence, the doctor should have a low threshold of suspicion if danger of an erroneous diagnosis, possibly unchallenged by a Registrar, is to be avoided. Once the body is disposed of by either burial or cremation, it may be too late to discover that a crime has been committed.

Cameron, in his presidential address to the BAFS, also discussed the serious consequences likely to arise in cases of misdiagnosis. While such an occurrence in cases of natural deaths is to be regretted, there are seldom any far-reaching consequences unless it be that a case is later treated as an unnatural death. But the mistake in certifying an unnatural death as due to natural causes can be much more serious. The law requires doctors not only to issue a death certificate but also to state the cause of death, whether a case is reportable to the Coroner or not. (Incidentally, old age is not accepted as a cause and refusal to certify a medical cause means invariably reference to the Coroner). All kinds of troublesome complications can ensue should unnatural cause be signed up as natural. Major crime may remain uninvestigated and there may also be problems of insurances, pensions and civil litigations, all stemming from incorrect or incomplete diagnosis of causes of death. This practice has been widely criticised in the medico-legal literature over the years - The Detection of Secret Homicide (Havard, 1960) is one example of a comprehensive review. Professor Cameron pointed also to recent surveys which have shown up to a 50% discrepancy rate between the clinical and autopsy recordings of death. He suggested, indeed recommended with some urgency, that the remedy for this is proper education of the future doctor during medical training in the pre-registration phase as an 'embryo' police surgeon, and in all branches of postgraduate medicine education. There is, he pointed out, great variation in the present teaching on the subject. (Cameron, 1980).

QUALIFICATION, SPECIALISATION AND FRAGMENTATION

Previous discussion connected with status and incumbency has led me to touch upon the confusing sets of medical qualifications displayed by members of the BAFM and the labelling of the forensic pathologist as a 'non-healer' engaged in a 'specialty at the margin'. Moreover, among the other stresses experienced by these practitioners (to be discussed in Chapters 5 and 6), is also cross-examination in Court which causes a great deal of dread and apprehension. The position of the doctor as a forensic witness must now be more closely examined, of which an orderly re-assessment of the maze of qualifications would appear to form an essential part. The main reason for this examination is the discrediting effect this often has upon the witness in terms of competence and career, to say nothing about the danger of having the profession debunked in the media. Parallel to a strictly scientific exposure runs the accusation that this (overworked and understaffed) profession does not sufficiently appear to take account of the social circumstances surrounding cause (Prior, 1989, pp. 371-373). An obvious consequence might well be, I would argue, the establishment of new professions to fill this gap, only to add to the fragmentation of a territory which was previously that of forensic pathology alone. Two examples will illustrate this trend. 1971 saw the birth of the youngest member of the family of Royal Colleges, the Royal College of Psychiatrists, which founded in that year a Section of Forensic Psychiatry to facilitate an increased understanding between lawyers and psychiatrists (Blair, 1974). But another most interesting example originated in the Argentine and found a write-up in the New Zealand Journal of Funeral Directors. It dealt with the disappearance of 90,000 Argentinians during the period of military rule in the 1970s. A team of young medical and anthropology students got to work one morning at a cemetery in the outskirts of Buenos Aires to painstakingly scrape away earth to expose decomposed cadavers, some in plastic bags or coffins and others simply dumped into the ground. It was slow and tedious work to find the clues of how each person died. A glint of metal suggested bullets were used; tiny fragments of skull bones indicated blows to the heads to produce fatal injuries. Their mentor was an American academic sent in 1984 to advise Argentina's Human Rights Commission on the scientific means to document abuses committed during the dirty war. Thus came into being the E.A.A.F., the Argentine Forensic Anthropology Team (Funeral Service Journal, 1989). How long before we shall be blessed, or some opinions might say cursed, with a Royal College of Forensic Anthropology? The Americans already have forensic anthropologists.

A GLANCE AT THE INTRICACIES OF MEDICAL EVALUATION
(see Blair, 1974, pp. 13-19)

The forensic pathologist comes into contact with lawyers and lay persons not always initiated in the intricacies of medical evaluations. The various letters which a doctor can legally append to the surname need to be correctly interpreted as to whether their number directly reflects theoretical knowledge, skill, experience and efficiency. Most of all, do they indicate forensic proficiency? The significance of degrees and letters operates as soon as the doctor qualifies, following a designated training curriculum and passing the prescribed examinations. Table A lists these in the order of increasing merit.

TABLE A - UK GRADUATING MEDICAL DEGREES

Awarding Body	Degree Obtained	Letters
Society of Apothecaries of London	Licentiate in Medicine and Surgery	L.M.S.S.A.
Conjoint Board of the Royal Colleges of Surgeons and Physicians, England	Member of the Royal College of Surgeons	M.R.C.S.
	Licentiate of the Royal College of Physicians	L.R.C.P.
Individual Universities	Bachelor of Medicine	M.B.
	Bachelor of Surgery	B.S.or B.Ch.

Source:
Adapted from Blair, D. (1974) *The Criminologist*, Vol.9. No.32, p14

University degrees are the most valuable but carry the fewest letters. Postgraduate degrees, as a next stage, can vary in their importance. Most cherished is membership of the Royal Colleges, achieved by doctors with ample experience in their specialty and passing requisite examinations. Surgeons become fellows, but fellowship of any other Royal College can be gained only after several years of membership and recognition of outstanding professional achievements. It is bestowed by the President and Council on a discretionary basis without the need to take a further examination. It is accepted that a young surgeon who has obtained a fellowship of his or her own Royal College would not be able to obtain a fellowship of any other Royal College until possibly in his or her forties. Universities also award postgraduate degrees in Medicine or Surgery, either by an acceptable thesis and/or searching examination. Furthermore, the Faculty of Radiologists grant higher degrees by examination and award a fellowship of the Faculty. Table B makes the position clear.

TABLE B - UK POSTGRADUATE MEDICAL DEGREES

Awarding Body	By Examination	Letters	By Election	Letters
Royal College of Surgeons	Fellowship of the Faculty of Anaesthetists of the Royal College of Surgeons	F.R.C.S. F.F.A.R.C.S.		
Royal College of Physicians	Membership	M.R.C.P.	Fellowship	F.R.C.P.
Royal College of Obstetricians & Gynaecologists	Membership	M.R.C.O.G.	Fellowship	F.R.C.O.G.
Royal College of Pathologists	Membership	M.R.C.Path.	Fellowship	F.R.C.Path.
Royal College of Psychiatrists	Membership	M.R.C.Psych.	Fellowship	F.R.C.Psych.
Royal College of General Practitioners	Membership	M.R.C.G.P.	Fellowship	F.R.C.G.P.
Individual Universities (with medical schools)	Master of Surgery Doctor of Medicine	M.S. or M.Ch. M.D.		
Faculty of Radiologists	Fellowship	F.F.R.		

Source:
Adapted from Blair, D. (1974) *The Criminologist*, Vol.9. No.32, p15

Dr. Blair, who is a Psychiatrist, informs us that 1974 was a year of grace for the medical profession in which it indulged in secret procedures of which the legal profession was probably unaware. It was a 'Secret Merit Award' to which, with the approval of Government, a National Health Service specialist may have been entitled. It is usually secretly bestowed on him/her by a hierarchy of peers. Neither degrees nor diplomas guarantee a doctor an increase in salary but a secret award, (which can be C, B, A and A+) accordingly to grade, can reach a figure of 7,000 pounds or more at the top scale. The unfairness of this arbitrary benefit is recognised but tolerated by the medical profession. It is not possible, officially, to discover which doctor gets which merit award. Lawyers certainly are kept guessing. There are, however, consultants who may have held Fellowships of Colleges for many years and do not get merit awards whilst there are others with only a few years of Membership of certain other Colleges who get C-grade awards or perhaps an even higher distinction.

In order to appreciate the value of forensic pathology qualifications in context, the existence of postgraduate medical diplomas must also be explained. The Diploma of Medical Jurisprudence (D.M.J.), which 44% of my respondents hold, is considered to be a reliable indicator among pathologists, police surgeons, prison medical officers and concerned others, that they have a certain amount of forensic knowledge in this field. Some highly qualified consultants, however, may well have received only meagre education and training in forensic medicine alone in their entire career. Table C sets out details of the recognised diplomas, to which, in the current climate of specialisation, others are added from time to time (of which, as indicated below, the new Diploma in Crime Scene Investigation approved in April, 1989 is one example).

Table C - Some Examples of UK Postgraduate Medical Diplomas

Awarding Body	Type of Diploma	Letters
Royal College of Surgeons	Orthodontics	D.Orth.
	Dental Public Health	D.D.P.H.
Conjoint Board of the Royal Colleges of Surgeons and Physicians, England	Public Health	D.P.H.
	Tropical Medicine and Hygiene	D.T.M. & H.
	Ophthalmology	D.O.
	Laryngology and Otology	D.L.O.
	Anaesthetics	D.A.
	Child Health	D.C.H.
	Industrial Medicine	D.I.M.
	Psychiatry	D.P.M.
Royal College of Obstetricians and Gynaecologists	Obstetrics	D.Obst.R.C.O.G.
Society of Apothecaries of London	Industrial Health	D.I.M.
	Medical Jurisprudence	D.M.J.
Royal College of Pathologists	Pathology	D.R.C.Path

Source:
Adapted from Blair, D. (1974) *The Criminologist*, Vol.9. No.32, p16

Other diplomas found to be held by forensic pathologists are the Diploma in Clinical Pathology, the Diploma in Criminology, the Diploma in Firearms Examination and the Diploma in Document Examination. As from April, 1989, following the completion of the planning stage, the new Diploma in Crime Scene Investigation will be available. This is a diploma sponsored by the Forensic Science Society (F.S.S.) and recognised by the then Council for National Academic Awards (C.N.A.A.). The F.S.S. Professional Awards Committee decided in 1985 to concentrate on those areas of forensic expertise not covered by other educational qualifications or formal course preparation and examination, and set up its own creation of professional qualifications in these fields. (Williams R.L., 1989).

There are seven diplomas for the forensic pathologist now and there will probably be more to come. If any specialist discovers a need not catered for, all he/she has to do is to submit a scheme to the F.S.S. Awards Committee for consideration. The general effect is likely to be a specialised qualification for the few who are so motivated to acquire this expertise on a voluntary basis, but not widely enough spread among the professional membership to be able to wrest (or in some cases reclaim) the expertise from those who perform it now and who came by it through areas of specialisation which made the fragmentation (and incidentally the loss of power and control) an inevitable consequence at the cost of a loss of status and prestige. In some cases functions not catered for by one Royal College may be assumed by another. Courts have needed to rely on valid evidence by psychiatrists, which caused the Royal College in 1971 to set up a Forensic Psychiatry Section. It also means a dependence on this expertise by forensic pathologists from other specialisations on occasions if the true cause of a crime or homicide and the circumstances leading up to the event are to be established. On an individual level, a forensic pathologist can become a member of an existing society whose aim it is to increase the mutual understanding and respect between his or her profession and those of lawyers, and so evidence a real interest in medico-legal matters. The British Academy of Forensic Sciences, The Medico-legal Society and the Forensic Science Society are organisations in point. The path to forensic proficiency begins with one or more degrees as indicated in Table A, followed by such postgraduate qualifications as the M.R.C.Path., the D.M.J. and other selected specialist diplomas and prolonged membership of one of the learned societies. It is also understood that research and publications enhance the road to Fellowship. The formal norms as here described will later make an interesting comparison with the actual (and perhaps typical) careers data obtained from my respondents.

THE PATHOLOGIST AS A WITNESS IN COURT

Many doctors, other than the most experienced in medico-legal matters, are apprehensive of cross examination when acting as a witness in Court. Forensic pathologists in particular may be called upon as experts for the defence or prosecution to give an opinion in a great variety of cases involving murder, homicide, violent crime, rape and those where injury occurs. It is unavoidable, therefore, that the question of assessing the legal significance of medical evidence arises. The professionals in the legal field need criteria by which to judge the status of the doctor, and so must take account of his/her years of experience and position as Consultant, Senior Registrar, Registrar or Houseman, as the case may be. In this context not only are degrees and diplomas relevant, but also interest (possibly evidenced by publication of research papers) and experience in matters forensic. The number of letters after a name are not by themselves a reliable measure of specific competence in a field and a person with higher degrees may not even bother to mention first degrees. Also posts in teaching hospitals are held in greater esteem than those in non-teaching hospitals, although an entirely academic career can leave a doctor lacking the very special experience needed by the Court. It is Dr. Blair's opinion, for example, that a general consultant pathologist who may have wide experience of ordinary causes of death would not easily replace a forensic pathologist in such cases as suspected murder, homicide and poisoning, which require a narrower but more precise knowledge of the field. Hence the wider use of general pathologists (recommended by the Brodrick Report in 1971) and the further reduction of the already small number of forensic pathologists is not favoured by the critics of this report. Dr. Blair, in common with later opinions by such experts as Professors Knight (1975), Cameron (1980), Mant (1986) among others in the profession, expressed his concern that the national facilities for forensic education are inadequate. (Knight, 1975).

Understandably, pathologists are highly sensitive about having their expert opinion challenged in a public arena, such as a Court, and exposed to the press. But much the more delicate and wide-ranging can be the problems which arise when a consultant pathologist acts for the defence. In many homicide cases, the trend is to prefer these to the employment of psychiatrists, as was the practice in previous years. Knight (1975, pp. 3-13) offers three reasons for this change: firstly, a greater awareness on the part of the legal profession that it can challenge the medical evidence gathered by the prosecution and can require a second autopsy as soon as the client is arrested; secondly, whilst there has been a decline in full-time forensic pathologists, the National Health Service has expanded pathology staff as such in the post-war period, although the available clinical experience was not also accompanied by a competence in the forensic field; and thirdly, the advent of legal aid has made it possible for those in need to enlist expert witnesses in their defence. Knight favours this turn of events since natural justice is better served if a second medical view on a homicide is available which may provide vital evidence in criminal trials to assist counsel for the defence. Moreover, the very fact that a fellow expert may challenge the findings of the prosecution pathologist largely prevents a belief that evidence is infallible, and may also stimulate the latter to meticulous examination of and reporting on a case.

This experienced Professor has a number of practical matters to disclose, one of which concerns the incidence of a second autopsy. Time and circumstances will influence this. For example, a local solicitor not used to major criminal charges may not be aware that early medical advice can be made available in a homicide case. The Coroner's autopsy as a part of the prosecution's evidence may have taken place and the body disposed of long before counsel's view that a second autopsy is possible. Cremation will not yet have taken place, but a possible demand for exhumation is beset with problems and is rare. Thus, a defence consultant may have no chance to examine the body. A criminal charge of homicide is usually conditional upon the autopsy results and no legal representative may have been appointed. At the same time, delay will grossly hinder the preservation of the physical evidence needed for the second autopsy. Even if refrigeration is good, a corpse deteriorates more rapidly after anatomisation at the first postmortem. Additionally, points out Knight, injuries such as abrasions or lacerations and the effects of any decomposition when a body is first discovered will make the job of the second pathologist even more difficult and his or her conclusions less valuable to the Court. At times, neither the presence and co-operation of the first pathologist nor his or her findings are available to the second, whose experience then plays a vital part in marshalling all the available details from the disordered body with not a clear idea of what he or she is seeking. If it is the case that parts of the corpse have been removed by the first pathologist, either as exhibits or for further examination (such as skin with stab and gunshot wounds or strangulation marks), these would have had to be preserved in formalin and so undergo change from their original condition. Parts such as fractured skull vaults or brains with attached membranes may have to be transported over long distances and cause delays for the defence pathologist before reporting. In other instances, body fluids such as urine, venous blood or stomach contents, may have been removed for dispatch to the Home Office Forensic Science Laboratory, leaving virtually nothing for the defence to present. At times, no postmortem may be possible due to lapse of time and all that is then left for the defence expert to get hold of is the available documents for supplying a summary of findings to the solicitor.

Thus, the relationship between pathologists for the prosecution and defence is quite a delicate one. Once in Court, shrewd counsel may ask the defence expert to sit close by for consultation when the prosecution medical evidence is probed. Occasionally, explains Knight, the pathologist on the opposite side takes exception to this practice, but, seen objectively, it balances the scales and should not be regarded as unethical behaviour or sniping as all witnesses are there to assist the Court in its endeavour to administer justice. It has on occasions been the case in the past that 'partisan emotions have run high and fair criticism degenerated into biased distortions'. Such harm is now avoided by the high standard of forensic expertise which does not tolerate any 'wild, unsubstantiated theorising and would be destroyed by the medical witness for the other side'. In some trials there is a distinct imbalance of expertise and reputation between defence and prosecution, accentuated, says Knight, by a lack of professional forensic pathologists. Very good clinical pathologists from hospitals can sometimes experience problems when medico-legal matters are at issue and it is then not logical to complain about the 'unequal size of guns' if better expertise should have been obtained. On the other hand, it has not been unknown in the past, for counsel to praise the stature, qualifications and impressive appointments of a charismatic medical witness who had the ability to out-shine the opinion of a lesser-famed pathologist. However, beneficial side-effects are possible even in contentious cases. Knight gives the example of how a controversial case of stabbing led to some hurried but quite valid research on the dynamics of knife wounds. He also relates from his personal experience that quotations from standard textbooks by well-known authors are resorted to by either side, but more often by the defence. In his view, it is an ethical obligation not to push this too far, since quotes can be taken out of context, can run counter to accepted opinion, can be from an outdated edition and, in any case, need not make something 'Professor X' said sacrosanct.

Knight quotes from a well-known forensic figure in this country (not named) the suggestion that there is a 'hard way' or an 'easy way' in which defence and prosecution pathologists may proceed. If by common consent each side is completely open with the other and discloses all findings and opinions, friction will be highly unlikely. The hard way is playing the cards close to the doctor's chest, as obviously lawyers are accustomed to do. Knight much prefers for the medical witness the frank way: 'doing it the hard way may well present the second pathologist with a shambles of a semi-decomposed body and be invited to get on with it'. Friction is also a possibility if pathologists on either side work in the same area or even meet up in the same postmortem room, but take a different view of a case in court. Diplomacy and tact is obviously needed in avoiding a reference to the case when working in such close proximity. One final point which possibly borders on the political is the attitude of the Home Office which disapproves of their retained consultants acting in a trial on opposite sides. It seems to the Professor (who is himself on the Register) that this Home Office disapproval arose from a Civil Service dictum that no section of the Establishment should be seen to criticise another, but would not be applicable here as the second pathologist is as much there to assist the Court as he is to help the legal representative of the accused to understand the medical evidence, and not to discredit a colleague. But, this Civil Service dictum, as followed by the Home Office, has been condemned by the B.M.A. as unduly restrictive and unethical, and with forensic departments in universities now severely reduced, it appears that it is no longer strongly adhered to.

THE PATHOLOGIST'S INVOLVEMENT IN MAJOR DISASTERS

Two American doctors (Reals & Cowan, 1979), in discussing the role of forensic pathology in mass disasters, point to the instant headlines of a plane crash whilst the carnage of the modern highway is largely ignored. Their paper recounts the Tenerife collision of two 747 jet aircraft in 1977 which resulted in the deaths of hundreds of people with whom, in a large modern city such as Santa Cruz, there were no facilities to cope. To be precise, 577 badly burned human bodies were recovered, needing under Spanish law either to be embalmed or buried within 48 hours after death. There were no refrigeration facilities for holding this large number of bodies so the dead underwent embalmment by Spanish morticians and were then placed in individually numbered coffins. As the large hanger at the airport was completely unsuitable for performing forensic tasks, and other facilities also inadequate, it was decided to move the bodies to the original boarding countries (America and Holland) following death certification and release by the Spanish authorities. The American bodies were dispatched one week after the accident and the necessary clear-up of the wreckage and the damaged runway.

The authors then discuss how the American authorities set about the forensic work concerned with identification. A task force of 120 individuals, consisting of an FBI fingerprint team, military medical and forensic dental experts and a graves registration unit was mobilised the same day to proceed under more ideal conditions with the meticulous task of identification. It took three full weeks to positively identify 212 of the dead, using body postmortem, X-ray film, fingerprinting, dental examination and total body inspection. Airline staff helped with records and documentation obtained from the families of the victims, enabling checks to be carried out in the large military mortuary at the Air Force Base in Delaware. Dental records alone allowed the largest number (some 70%) to be identified. Combined with fingerprinting, some 80% of the persons could be traced. California State requires all drivers to be fingerprinted and since most of the victims came from there, this helped in at least 10% of the cases to name them. Unidentified remains were buried on a Californian Common Site in individually numbered graves, but allowing for reburial elsewhere should later identification come to light. It speaks highly for modern forensic science skills that 220 badly mutilated bodies could be positively identified.

These writers then draw attention to the long-standing prediction by forensic experts that widely spaced jet plane disasters would find aviation authorities unprepared. This accident confirmed that prediction, although the Spanish authorities tried very hard to comply with time limits, distance, resources and the ambit of Spanish law, as well as dealing with the immediate needs of 69 people who survived the crash. An ad-hoc assembly of forensic experts, together with American Military personnel, was alerted to travel long-distance on a weekend to reach the location needing help. The forensic involvement as a humanitarian activity (from which clearly embalmers cannot be excluded) (see Bibliography - Major Disasters) brought much comfort to the victims' families, as well as assisting the legal formalities that inevitably followed. Since our culture requires the careful identification of dead bodies if mass burial is to be avoided, efficient disaster management is rudimentary. Unlike the long-standing expertise in this country evolved through the good offices and active participation of the old-established funeral directors, Kenyon Securities PLC, now a world leader in this field, there was at the time no such group in the US to function quickly in an emergency other than the forensic team of the Armed Forces. The authors expect, either through human action or mechanical failure, mass casualties to increase in the future and suggest establishment of a worldwide forensic pathology system, sponsored either privately by industry or by government, as the obvious lesson to be drawn from the Tenerife disaster.

Some twenty years on, a Federal Emergency Management Agency (FEMA) has been in place since 1979, with the aim of consolidating the Nation's emergency-related programmes. It has regional offices in ten large cities and its principal activities provide for an integrated operational capability to respond to and recover from the consequences of a disaster, regardless of its cause, in partnership with other Federal agencies, State and local organisations and the private sector. The FEMA funds emergency programmes, offers technical guidance and training and deploys Federal resources in times of catastrophic disaster to constitute a broad-based programme to protect life and property and provide recovery assistance after a disaster. So, an essential need is now being met. (FEMA, 1999).

CONCLUDING OBSERVATIONS

Chapters 3 and 4 are designed to provide a basic framework for those interested parties who aim to discover more about the ways and means of a profession whose fluctuating fortunes have taken a downward turn over the years. Indeed, the Weberian view that medical science need not be restricted to the medically qualified, may well be shared by a wider public. This study endeavours in particular to allow the uninitiated insider to look at the profession of death and to reveal what the forensic experts think of themselves. In attempting this task its segments have been operationally defined, dramaturgical scenery constructed in work settings, attitudes revealed and the various connected associations identified.

In tracing the vicissitudes of this profession in a historical context, it has been a key purpose to discover a range of attaching stigmas, some largely manifest, others merely potential and not so blatantly obvious that they could not be elicited by closer examination on the part of the researcher. The indicators that taint, place a slur or discredit were so far mainly obtained, drawn or inferred from a variety of secondary sources forcing themselves into view at various stages of the discussion. The chapters now to follow continue the illumination of the insider look, but in a form which will test the central hypothesis (that an 'occupational stigma' is present) with the help of the survey data collected from these doctors.

CHAPTER 5

HOW THE DEAD PROVIDE A LIVING - SELF-PERCEPTION OF ANATOMISTS' WORK

There is a general awareness among most of us that the concept of 'career' is still an elite institution in Western society if the term signifies a graduated sequence of increasing responsibilities attaching to an occupation or profession. Careers imply not only patterns and directions, choice and change, often associated with certain 'rites of passage' (an anthropological term denoting transition to a new status in the life-cycle of a person or group) but also a way by which a person is judged and, more significantly, judges himself or herself. Although the word careers implies this elevated position in society, there are certain occupations and professions which are beset by contradictions and dilemmas of status. Such occupational 'marginality' (to borrow Robert Park's words (1928) some 60 years ago to describe disaffiliated immigrants) allude frequently to death work also and anatomists in particular. Many years of study for the pathologist there may be, but then in recent literature to be referred to as 'the weevil in the flour sac of Medicine', and more humorously to be described as a despicable creature vilified by his interest in the morbid, depraved by prolonged exposure to evisceration and dismemberment, must be disconcerting and disillusioning for a member of this specialty. (Surgeon-writer Richard Selzer, 1981).

What of self-perception? Doctors have it. We all normally have it, an awareness of, and attitudes toward, our own psychic and biologic person. Such perception is part of the process of socialisation and learned in social interaction through the medium of language. It was Mead (1934) who alerted us to the possibility of putting oneself mentally in the place of another when assuming a role, and Blumer, a student of Mead and Chicago School affiliate, who took to elaborating his mentor's ideas, in particular suggesting that what is meaningful to oneself is not so much reacting to stimuli as fashioned by various forms of interaction. (Blumer, 1962). These concepts enabled us better to understand an individual's life events in terms of careers and the way in which subjectively attitudes, aspirations and actions are linked objectively to opportunities and circumstances. During the years of the pioneering sociologist Hughes (1958, p. 129), with his prolific output of writings on work, occupations and professions, and Blumer, along came the inventive Goffman to coin his magical 'mini-concepts', whose point of departure from the (by now) impoverished symbolic-action-tradition, was the theatrical perspective of face-to-face relationships, defining situation and managing impression. (Drew & Wootton, Eds., 1988). The dramaturgical aspects of forensic pathology work, as also the frankest revelations about the subjective experiences of these incumbents to be presented here, will lend further credibility to the concepts from the masters of social theory named above and enrich such supporting evidence as already exists.

The discussion in the previous chapter leaves one in little doubt that the profession has in recent years acquired a damaged, if not a spoiled, identity. The survey responses now to follow deal in part with such critical issues as lack of recruitment, the aging of specialists and their vulnerability in Court, which continue to bother the leaders and members of this group. Also addressed are more personal questions that reach deeply into the self of these incumbents to present a fearful reminder that by the very nature of their activity they are themselves merely mortal. But before embarking on the analysis of this data, findings will be presented from a random selection of doctors who had deliberately chosen other specialisms than the forensic pathology field, and so illustrate by the reasons they give how post mortem and related work can be vilified with additional stigmas planted in the public mind.

TESTAMENTS OF REJECTION -
CLINICIANS DEMAND BODIES WITH SOULS

This part investigates how doctors not trained in Forensic Pathology feel about this specialism. The purely random selection of doctors here - 36 individuals in all - is not in the strictest statistical sense intended to serve as a control group. It is much more a barometer of antipathy towards a specialty that is apparently devoid of a patient orientation and healing properties. The responses were gathered through personal and patients' contacts (the latter willingly presenting my questionnaire to their doctors), with the sole aim to discover (a) why in their opinion recently qualified doctors do not wish to specialise in the field of forensic pathology; and (b) why these respondents themselves have not been attracted to this particular branch of sub-disciplines. The personal details requested from this group were confined to age, gender and medical speciality.

Respondents' Specialties	M	F	Gender	Age Groups % (M/F)
Orthopaedic Surgery	10	-	Male 72%	25 - 44 58
General Practice	8	4		
Radiology	1	-	Female 28%	45 - 65 31
Psychogeriatrics	1	-		
Paediatrics	1	2		65+ 11
Anaesthesia	-	1		
Community Medicine	-	1	Ages Male %:	Ages Female %:
Opthalmology	2	-		
Cardiology	1	-	25 - 44 56	25 - 44 . . . . Nil
Psychiatry	2	2		
	—	—	45 - 65 19	45 - 65 14
	26	10	65+ 3	65+ . . . . . .
	—	—		

First of the two questions addressed to the Non-Forensic Pathologists:

It has been posited that there is currently a reluctance of newly-qualified doctors opting to specialise in the field of Forensic Pathology. Please give your opinion why this might be so.

In analysing the data a fivefold classification from the responses is attempted.

1. Lack of Inspiration or Information during Training.
a) Lack of Information concerning this speciality.
b) Undergraduate pathology lectures not inspiring.
c) Little undergraduate teaching to whet one's appetite for the subject.
d) In my day in college, it was a dull subject taught without inspiration.
e) Exposure to forensic pathology rather limited during medical training.
f) We were left in ignorance about the nature of this kind of work.

2. Negative Experiences.
a) Option unattractively portrayed.
b) Hated pathology at MD exams.

3. Obstacles encountered in choosing this Subject as a Career.
a) Difficulties with finding a suitable training position.
b) Too much competition for places on training schemes.
c) Too few jobs available and a career structure not obvious.

4.   Actual Dislike of Forensic Pathology Work.
a)   Forensic pathology remote, gruesome and unrelated to day-to-day medicine.

5.   Positive Choices in other Directions.
a)   Students enter Medicine to treat live patients.
b)   Subject too far removed from the mainstream of clinical work.
c)   Pathology itself has been the more popular of choices.
d)   4. a) above also relates to this category.

Comments:
    given the variation of the specialties of these respondents, the expressed sentiments about the subject matter of forensic pathology have been remarkably similar across age and gender of the respondents. Unattractive presentation of this sub-discipline at medical school, if at all offered as a choice, a shortage of training places, lack of career structure as well as the acknowledged gruesome nature of the work, show clearly through as the perceived reasons for giving this specialty a miss. Not a single response expressed retrospective regret that forensic pathology had not been chosen, although a small number (some 5%) would have considered this option if their 'appetite had been whetted' at the point of making a choice.

Second question addressed to Non-Forensic Pathologists:

Please can you say why Forensic Pathology has not attracted you as an area in which to specialise.

It is once more convenient to summarise responses into categories and limit them to six this time.

1.   Patient Involvement a significant variable.
a)   Enjoy treating patients and seeing the result of the treatment.
b)   My concept of practising Medicine was (said a retired GP) to treat, heal and comfort the sick.
c)   In forensic pathology work there is no continuity of care.
d)   I value patient contact and feel I am at my best when working with children and their parents.

2.   Career Information and Opportunities.
a)   Small number of jobs available.

b)   Minimal undergraduate exposure.
c)   Lack of suitable training posts.

3.   Distasteful Work Content.
a)   Dislike of dissecting specimens and performing autopsies.
b)   Too squeamish for Forensic Pathology.
c)   Prefer to use my technical skills in surgery.

4.   Unsuitable Working Conditions.
a)   Preference for shared work rather than isolation.
b)   Working conditions (irregular hours, pay differentials, often the work environment) known to be poor.
c)   No choice to go into private practice at that time (New Zealand Doctor).
d)   Not keen to embark on a life in the Civil Service (American Doctor).

5.   Stressful ancillary Requirements for Success.
a)   Cross examination in open Court can be very stressful.
b)   A great deal of learning of law in addition to Pathology required.
c)   I don't wish to spend much time giving evidence in Court.

6.   Adverse Images of the Job.
a)   I am repelled by close contact with crime and violence over my whole   working life.
b)   Forensic pathology deals with thoroughly unattractive situations and people.
c)   This specialty appeals only to a minority.
d)   Clearly an area of Medicine too close to the darker side of people's problems.
e)   One is isolated from colleagues as well as involved with ghoulish murder cases and there seems to be no positive aspect, such as Preventive Health.
f)   One assumes an increased mortality among those practising Forensic pathology (although this may be a trend relating to other doctors as well).

Comments: -
    Patient contact and the healing aspect of their work is clearly of great importance whatever the age group, gender and specialist category. Equally, the indication is that the harrowing image of forensic pathology work has not attracted them at the point of choice, whilst the essential

legal studies and Law Court appearances also have no appeal. The one exception was a woman General Practitioner who, although she enjoys clinical medicine, sees forensic work as an interesting specialty and has actually worked as a Police Surgeon for a couple of years and done post-graduate work in forensic medicine.

Concluding Observations: -

Here and there in the responses to both questions one notices from the occasional chance remark by these doctors that a propensity to stigmatize exists as the following examples will show:

> *"...a detached scientific attitude towards Pathology and Morbid Anatomy is essential, and a twisted mind to enjoy Forensic Pathology in particular..."*
>
> (Female GP, 67 years of age);

> *"...there is also an impression that 'unusual talents' are required. I think a lot of people would find it very unpleasant..."*
>
> (Male GP, 45 years of age);

> *"...Forensic Pathology is a sub-speciality that is deeply disturbing to one's own psychic equilibrium..."*
>
> (Male, specialising in Psychiatry, 46 years of age.)

> *"...presumably appealing to only a 'small group' as it has little to do with sick, live people..."*
>
> (Male, Orthopaedic Surgeon, 31 years of age);

> *"...those who choose it seem to wish to deal with the unhappier and more unpleasant face of medical life..."*
>
> (Female GP, 51 years of age).

As far as these non-forensic pathologists are concerned, the whole tenor of the views expressed attaches unmistakably an avowed label of deviance to the profession of forensic pathology, and to its individual members the stigma of a spoiled identity (to borrow Goffman's term). The responses show the choosers of options on offer to the medical orthodoxy of healers to regard those 'different others' as distinctly atypical careerists from the accepted norm, if not actually somewhat peculiar types. Moreover, there is a clear inference in the main on the part of the live patient opters that they themselves are to be seen as the normal ones in the profession of doctor. By comparison, the data analysis now to follow, will reveal how forensic pathologists themselves have come to make their specialist choice, reflecting as it does no circumstances that might substantiate the clinicians' notion that there is a distinctive breed making the dead their life's work.

THE FORENSIC PATHOLOGIST'S SELF -
Drawing the Ore from the Data

In this part the focus is on the forensic pathologist, who will emerge with a dual social identity that reflects self-perceived attributes of normality, together with an acute awareness that the image of a so-called spoiled identity is also there. In other words, one envisions in the two-phased sociologically depicted self the individual as a uniquely creative, experiencing biological being alongside a socially constrained, regulated, predictable creature. (Plummer, 1985).

IDENTITY OF A PROFESSION

The previous chapter has shown the steps that must be trodden to qualify and in due course attain in some cases Home Office recognition. As individual aspirants, a degree of occupational mobility may be an essential endeavour - or as Durkheim would have it: 'For to live by a metier one must have clients, and he must sally forth from his house to find them...' (Durkheim, 1902)...though they be quite dead when he has found them (my words). But as Hughes reminds us (1958, pp. 44-45), there is another kind of mobility relating to the standing of an organised group to which members belong, that of the professional association itself. This profession already experienced problems in 1971, when the Brodrick Committee was appointed. An adequate number of forensic pathologists was not available to the police and the whole service needed to be put on a sounder footing. Chapters 1 and 2 traced the problem and analysed the causes of the deteriorating position into which this profession has been allowed to slide. Leading members are not to blame for they have in articles in their journals and in meetings expressed their concern over the years. As we have seen, by 1984, the alarming state of the service had come to the attention of Parliament and the then Home Secretary established a Working Party to review the arrangements at the time and make recommendations with regard to organisation and funding;

appointments and conditions of service;   training and quality assurance.
As mentioned, the recommendations of the Wasserman Report (April
1989) have now been put into operation.

INTERNALS AND EXTERNALS OF THE CORPSE - DISTINGUISHING SPECIALTIES

Before analysing the data, it is important to reaffirm the distinction
between a pathologist per se and a pathologist in the forensic field. The
former as physician is interested in the causes, processes and effects of
disease. He explains the living being by examination of the corpse and as
soon as the dead cease to be human, they no longer hold any interest for
him. That at any rate is Dr. Gonzalez-Crussi's view, himself a
pathologist, and he adds that 'the long and continued list of contributions
of pathological anatomy to medicine, stands as proof - a fact not
researched enough by epistemologists - that, in conducting inquiries, it
often pays to bridle the horse by the tail'. (Gonzalez-Crussi, 1985, p. 65).
Pathologists as such are essentially laboratory people, described more
vividly in phenomenological terms by Dr. Ashley thus:

> *'Each working morning three or four naked corpses lie on
> the gleaming slabs equipped with hoses, sponges, bowls and
> knives, awaiting the duty pathologist. The examination probably
> takes about an hour, and is conducted with meticulous respect.
> The external appearance is particularly important in forensic
> work but less so in hospital cases. In the latter, it is the internal
> organs which are of interest and these are removed through a
> long incision from the pelvis to the neck. Individual organs are
> inspected and weighed: tubes such as the intestine, the windpipe,
> the bile duct, the coronary arteries, followed and opened through
> their length. Abscesses, tumours, blood clots, haemorrhages,
> deformed heart valves will all be noted and anything unusual
> discussed with colleagues from neighbouring tables.'* (Ashley,
> 1987).

Whether the eventual findings explain the anatomical cause of death
and tally with the clinical diagnosis, or whether perhaps obvious clues
have been missed, it is the post-mortem room or even the laboratory that
might well be regarded as the medicine's 'Court of Final Appeal',
according to Ashley's view. From a sociological perspective, status

enhancement through this quality control (and thus in a sense medical policing) enables the pathologist to elevate what is often thought of by physicians as 'the dirty and obnoxious work in medicine', if not also reminding graduates of their dissection routines during student days. So, proudly then, the pathologists see themselves as the 'Doctors' doctors in their perceived role as consultants to the clinicians.

As to forensic pathologists, with whom we are already well acquainted, they are likewise not seen as healers by the medical fraternity. Worse still is the dilemma when it is questioned whether indeed they are to be regarded as 'doctors'. They too act in a medical policeman's role, not only when they are on opposite sides in Court, and interpretation of evidence varies - as in a case where three defence pathologists performed separate autopsies on the same body (Mant, 1986, Med.Sci.Law) - but also when there are discrepancies between an empirical setting of a homicide and the evaluators in the laboratory. Forensic, as other pathologists, are forever sensitive to forms of quality control and watch-dogging as they do not relish unpleasant publicity, becoming 'frozen out' from colleague networks or possibly infringing ethical codes. Prestige-wise, forensic pathologists have now been on a downward spiral over a period of 35 years, following the loss of their earlier historical status as medical fact finders and mediators between the basic sciences and their application to matters clinical. The distinction of the internals and the externals as sub-specialties tend often to become blurred in the environment of the mortuary. This has latterly found practical expression by the insistence of the term 'Forensic Medicine' for Forensic Pathology in some medical faculties of teaching hospitals. (Duckworth, 1989).

In answer to the question whether forensic pathologists would like to be part of the clinical team, Professor Green feels that up to a point, the answer is yes. 'For example, I not infrequently will examine a child with suspicious injuries to back up a paediatrician's suspicion that it might have been abused. My other colleagues have similar interests to a greater or lesser degree. However, clinical forensic medicine on the whole is the parlieu of the general practitioner/police surgeon or the accident and emergency consultant. We do not examine living patients on a regular basis, and so we would not wish to extend our incursions into clinical medicine further'. (Green, 1998).

Having earlier shown how Ashley perceives pathology work per se, Gonzalez-Crussi's view on forensic pathology now forms a suitable comparison, demonstrating how this anatomist-writer (like the revered Goffman) manages to join words to sculpt refined meanings.

'The anatomical concept of disease has long consolidated, but its cultivation still requires as much conviction and scientific zeal as stomach. Perhaps in no other area is this more true than in the field of forensic pathology. There would be much to say of its proud record as a science. The investigation of poisoning, for example, extends from the naive Chinese coroners who used to test for poisons by placing a fistful of rice in a cadaver's mouth, then feeding it to chickens to observe untoward effects...There would even be much to say of the moral contribution of this science, since an essential part is...to uphold the rule of justice in human transactions.'

When physical death is perceived, the marks and signs of it are normally taken as visible 'on' and 'in' the body and viewed as a container of all manner of facts, explanations and data on mortality. (Prior, 1989, p19). It is this aspect of visibility and observation in forensic pathology work that is so well brought out by Gonzalez-Crussi's further expressed thoughts:

'...but our concern is here exclusively with externals. To the forensic pathologist, the outward structure of death is usually the horrid effect of violence on the frailty of the human body. The field of study is men, women and children, cut into small bits, bludgeoned into amorphous, bloody tatters, carbonized by high temperatures, immersed in tanks of corrosive acids, bloated by prolonged immersion in water, half eaten by rats, tunnelled by maggots, skinned by abrasives, blue from asphyxia, cherry red from carbon monoxide, inconspicuously pierced with ice picks, or blown into irrecoverable shreds by industrial explosions. I confess to lacking the mettle requisite for looking beyond these externals into legal, moral and scientific considerations. Yet one aspect of these externals I find fascinating, and it is a central preoccupation of the forensic pathologist: it is the systematic study of the formalism of death, the careful canvassing of posture, gesture, and all extrinsic circumstances that surround individual deaths...the ways of entering into this world are limited, but those of leaving it seem infinite...'. (Gonzalez-Crussi, 1985, p67)

FORENSIC PATHOLOGISTS - Population and Response Rate

Total Number of Forensic Pathologists (England & Wales)	48 (100%)
Non-responders giving no Reason, although requested	12 (25%)
Non-responders offering an Explanation or Reason	9 (19%)
Total Number of Responders	**27 (56%)**

> **Note:**
> The Source for the Total Number of Forensic Pathologists in England and Wales is the List of Fellows and Members of the British Association in Forensic Medicine as obtained from the Hon. Secretary. There has been a stable membership for the last ten years.

Non-responders' Reasons for not completing the Questionnaire:

1. Overwhelming pressure of work. If another copy could be sent the respondent would endeavour to help in the next few weeks.

2. This answer claims that my questionnaire has not been received and the respondent would be pleased to have another.

3. Research questionnaires are no longer this doctor's flavour of the month and he is sorry to be the wrong person to be asked for a reply.

4. Some of the data requested seems to be of a personal and confidential nature to which this respondent is reluctant to reply...and more so as these were to be computerised...

5. From the Consultant's Secretary: Dr. X. has asked me to let you know that he is relatively inexperienced on the forensic side and does not feel able to complete the long questionnaire.

6. The respondent stated succinctly that he does not complete questionnaires of this nature.

7. Another claims that the questionnaire had never been received. (No response to the replacement copy sent either).

8. The questionnaire will not be completed as the information requested is personal and confidential.

9. The doctor states that all information regarding sudden deaths carried out in the department is strictly confidential and not therefore divulged to persons other than medical colleagues with a special interest in the case.

Observations: -

Of 21 respondents (out of 48) who have not completed the questionnaire, the 9 above have at least given reasons after receiving two follow-up letters. Even so, considering that this is an overworked profession (which hard evidence has confirmed), the completion of the questionnaire from 56% of the whole population of Forensic Pathologists in the country practising at that time (and not just a sample) may be considered a good response. Those asking for a second copy of the questionnaire (answers 1,2 and 7) did not complete this copy either. As to answer 4, the small number involved and the qualitative nature of the questions obviated the need for computer analysis. A special letter advised the doctor to this effect. Concerning answer 5, only one person with this respondent's initials could be traced on the Home Office List on which normally only experienced forensic pathologists appear. Finally, non-responder 9 has been advised that the medical causes of death are not a part of this research, but this has not resulted in obtaining the information originally requested. The following additional comments regarding this survey may be helpful:

a) The number of 48 Forensic Pathologists was made up from the BAFM Register as already advised on the previous page. This source is supplemented by doctors from the Home Office List.

b) Each of the questionnaires sent to respondents was accompanied by a personal letter explaining in concise terms the rationale of the research. A special paragraph also stressed the confidentiality with which the names of persons and names of institutions were to be treated.

c) Non-responders (21 out of 48) were sent a follow-up and if no reply to that a final letter asking for reasons which has attracted the foregoing 9 replies.

d) To those who had not responded (21 of the 48), a follow up letter
    was sent and if then no reply, a further letter requesting that reasons
    be given for their non-response. This has attracted 9 replies.

Profiling the Population of Respondents.

Place of Birth:

UK	S. Africa	Australia	Singapore	India	Shri-Lanka	
21	1	1	1	1	2	=27

Age Groups:

(Male & Female)	Gender Division	Average Age
24 - 44 . . . . 26%	Male: 26	Male: 52.5 years
45 - 65 . . . . 63%		
65+. 11%	Female: 1	Female: 30 years

Marital Status:

Married	Divorced or Separated	Single
23	2	2

85% plus 15% (4) make up the 100%

Children:

4 or more	3 Children	2 Children	1 Child	Childless
11	7	5	2	2

85% have two or more children

Ethnic Background:

White Caucasian:	Asian
25 (92%)	2

Religious Affiliations:

Church of England	14
Roman Catholic	3
Methodist	2
Non-conformist Congregational	1
Presbyterian	1
Hindu	1
Buddhist	1
Non-practising	4

Church of England (52%) slightly outnumbers all the other categories.

Age at which formal Forensic Pathology Training was completed: -
Stating a definite age between 31 and 40 years
21 (appr. 77%.)

Assumed average age for completing formal training
36 years but the majority of the respondents stated that further studies had been undertaken later (such as for the Diploma in Medical Jurisprudence). Most of the answers also attached such additional comments as: -

a)   Education is a continuing process;
b)   Education finishes only upon retirement;
c)   One assumes if asked, many would say it does not finish even then.

Occupation of Spouse:
Housewife (or no occupation given)	13
Nursing Sister or Nurse, full or part-time	2
Medical Practitioner (various Branches)	4
Secretary or Medical Secretary	2
Professional Artist	1
Laboratory Technician (when working)	1
School Mistress (retired)	1
Dietician	1

52% of the wives are not in paid employment and at least 9 work in a medical or related field (36%), leaving just the two wives employed as Secretary and Artist, and the School Mistress, now retired.

Leisure Activities of Forensic Pathologists: -
Age Group 25 - 44:
Natural History, Photography, Writing, Reading, Running, Skating, Swimming, Dog-walking, Eating-out, Visiting Pubs, Home & Family, Orchid-growing, Music, Travel, Languages, Sailing, Hockey, Model Trains, Walking.

Age Group 45 - 65:
Cricket, Carpentry, Music, Hockey, Running, Golf, Reading, TV and Radio, Homelife, Climbing, Cycling, Gardening, Wine, Silver, Cars, Boats, Model Railways, Farming, Antique and Art Collecting, Writing & Journalism, Walking, Photography, Snooker, Contract Bridge, Motoring, Reading, Judo, Mineralogy,

Literature, Military History, Choral Singing, Fell Walking, Church Affairs, Rotary, Model Ships.

Age Group over 65:
Fly-fishing, Philately, Gardening, Walking, Piano-playing, Golf, Cooking, Shooting, Holidays.

<u>Some Observations on the Profile.</u>

If one could identify a typical forensic pathologist from this profile at all, the weight of the data from a 56% response rate of the population indicates that the typical incumbent is likely to be a white male Caucasian, born in the UK, in his early sixties and a father with a spouse from the medical fraternity. Formal training would normally have been completed by the age of 40, although further study is frequently undertaken in such specialised areas as forensic serology, histopathology or even graphology and document interpretation. All doctors claimed to have leisure interests but are constrained by time, and religious affiliations could be identified as predominantly Church of England.

<u>Outward Approximations towards a Stereotype.</u>

The profile projected from the predominant outward characteristics shown above is a good match with the forensic pathologist that the media has presented us with in the recent past. Of course there will be deviations, clearly due to differences emerging from the facesheet data on display. But, much the more significant will be the subjective experiences of their work and the values, attitudes and opinions reflected in the responses. Before attempting this analysis, some annotations on the profile need to be made. One notes the very few women in this profession not (according to Dr. Green, 1990) because the males wish to dominate, but more so because the limited career prospects and the irregular hours make it unattractive to females. One observes also a trend towards an aging profession of which leading members have long been aware, but their concern has only recently gained formal recognition in the Wasserman Report mentioned earlier. There is an indication of the need for strong family support and a possible desire for the company of children as a therapeutic alleviation to the stressful work. (70% of the respondents have 3 or more children). No significant active religious participation is apparent, evidenced by such accompanying remarks as: C of E lapsed; very loose C of E; non-practising; or, more agnostic as time goes by. If spouses are gainfully employed, this is likely to be in some medical field. As to leisure activities, somewhat peripheral to the work experience in forensic medicine, this research did not attempt to investigate the finer correlations between stressful work and recreation, although the broad age group divisions do reveal an unusually wide range of interests. But no definite association could be detected that connects the work of a forensic pathologist per se directly with the type of leisure pursuits undertaken.

THE REALITY OF AGGREGATE STIGMAS -
A Feasible Proposition to be tested by qualitative Means

The details gathered together in the previous chapters and the discussion in this one so far make it quite feasible to erect a central hypothesis which has already earned credibility from a large variety of secondary sources and the fears expressed in speeches and writings about the declining state of this profession by a number of its leaders. To subject this central proposition to further scrutiny, six searching questions have been put to these doctors country-wide and the respondents encouraged to write down as it comes into their minds their innermost feelings about the issues posed. To restate, they touch on career choice and specialisation, the grisly nature of the work, consciousness of incumbents' own mortality, vulnerability as a witness in Court and perceptions of the public image the profession has. Space here can be spared only for edited extracts from the original research, which elaborates more fully the feelings, fears and concerns grounded in the data.

THE PROPOSITION

FORENSIC PATHOLOGISTS, BEING BY REASON OF THEIR WORK, MEMBERS OF A SMALL SELECT AND SEEMINGLY HIGH-PRESTIGE PROFESSIONAL GROUP, EXPERIENCE (nevertheless) AN ACUTE STATUS AMBIGUITY ON THE GROUNDS OF AMBIVALENT IDENTITY ARISING FROM A LACK OF FEEDBACK, RECOGNITION, IDEOLOGY, AS WELL AS LAW COURT TRAUMAS AND UNSOCIAL DEMANDS OF TIME, WHICH

IN CONSEQUENCE RESULT IN A NEGATIVE PERCEPTION (and frequently self-perception) OF THEIR SOCIAL LOCATION WITHIN OTHER MEDICAL PROFESSIONS IN PARTICULAR AND IN A DISTORTED PUBLIC IMAGE GENERALLY.

This proposition will be subject to tests by means of qualitative survey responses in Chapter 6.

CHAPTER 6

THE FORENSIC PATHOLOGIST'S IDENTITY - FOCUS ON THE QUALITATIVE SURVEY RESPONSES

Section I. Generation of Interest in Forensic Pathology and eventual Choice.

> *"...born and brought up in a hospital where my father was the superintendent, I became interested in morbid anatomy after (secretly) watching post mortems through an air brick in the mortuary when I was aged ten..."* (Professor W.).

Before constructing a question why someone might be interested in forensic pathology and opt to specialise in such an unwholesome field, a researcher might well ask whether there is a fascination with death, a macabre interest in seeing blood, perhaps a slant towards investigative matters or an inherent aggressive instinct, later redirected to the cut and thrust of legal questioning and debate in Court. Whilst the seeds of aggression or a morbid anatomic curiosity might well be present in a small number, the data obtained yielded a bewildering variety of reasons, best divided into two main parts and conveniently summarised under categorised headings.

How early interest emerged: Appr. %

1.   Parent associated with medicine or law   11

2.   Interest in science and laboratory work at school   22

3.   No specific early interest in medico-legal matters   67

Note:
The words 'early interest' refer mainly to pre-medical school life.

Later choice to specialise in the work: Appr. 70%

1. Medical School:

my original interest in pathology was sparked off at Cambridge and St. Thomas' Hospital;

interested in the diagnostic side of medicine, got 'hooked' during my training;

attracted by histopathology - it is more precise than clinical medicine and has a high status;

attended a guest lecture by Professor Simpson and emerged determined to become a forensic pathologist;

my undergraduate training offered a full course in forensic medicine;

my external examiner, the late Professor Sir Sidney Smith, encouraged me to specialise in this field;

interested in forensic medicine but not my original ambition, which was to become an obstetrician and gynaecologist;

I went to medical school to become a doctor in order that I could then specialise as a forensic pathologist and eventually get on the Home Office List;

Professor Webster first generated my interest as an undergraduate;

my interest dates back to student days and on return from National Service was advised by the Dean to enter this branch;

was always interested in pathology as a medical student and forensic pathology seemed a rewarding challenge and had benefits to the community;

2. Derived Interest: Appr. 22%

> *became involved in forensic pathology as a young Government Medical Officer in Malawi and later Zambia as an initial interest and then never to return to the previous role;*

> *as a consultant Neuropathologist had an interest in and desire to research head injuries which required autopsies for the Coroner who then asked me to take on cases of crime associated with such injuries;*

> *my interest is morbid anatomy, but could not choose it as no one else was available to deal with the forensic side;*

> *my original interest and challenge was aided and abetted by necropsy work as an NHS Consultant Pathologist, and later work for a Coroner got me more and more involved with the local Constabulary. This mainly because the local Home Office Pathologist was some distance away;*

3. Chance Vacancies: Appr. 8%

> *a chance vacancy at my own medical school drew me into forensic pathology and I decided to try it for a year because I liked the Head of Department...:*

> *chance: my first appointment was with a Home Office Pathologist who took me with him on many 'call-outs'. My later career after more study took me to Canada as a consultant in this field for the Department of Justice.*

How career choices emerged

In questions of occupational choice, the early endeavours of the Americans Ginzberg (1951), Blau (1956), and Super (1957) spring to mind. In their theorising the individual is subject to a process of stages in the course of which he or she becomes gradually aware of his or her interests and capabilities and the social environment within the (as yet) vague conception might later come to fruition. As is usual, pioneering ideas attract criticism by those who attempt to refine them. So in this case, Ginzberg's scheme, though narrowing choices through time, ties it too closely to age and the US educational system. Roberts (1975), a British sociologist, does not favour the stage process at all and instead stresses the importance of opportunity as a key concept. Super believes in the self-concept when a decision is made, but this is to be related to work roles for the achievement of an equilibrium. Holland (1959) argues similarly. His and Super's concept may be seen as a 'chicken-egg' approach. Work and personality may sometimes be compatible, although it is also true that the latter and the self-concept exhibited are often shaped by the nature of the work. Others have also made useful contributions to theory (Musgrave, 1974, for example, attaches great importance to anticipatory socialisation). By and large such pre-work influences cover family, class, education, gender, race, peer group and the media. These variables may then be related to the person in terms of attributes such as his or her aspirations and knowledge, and these linked to the environment - the occupational structure and finding a place in it.

The intention in presenting a brief view of where we are with our knowledge of occupational choice (and 'choice' is not always the appropriate term as not every seeker has a choice), is merely to relate it to the survey responses of the doctors in two ways: firstly, to show that parental and school influences played a part but not a large part in the emergence of early notions of choice and also, on this evidence at least, that a large body of school leavers had not even then formulated a definite vocational objective. Possible reasons may be (a) lack of exploration because students were immersed in the educational demands needed for advanced studies, and/or (b) that no suitable vocational guidance was available to them. Secondly, there is the question of what motivating influence it is that causes a doctor to opt for a particular speciality. Whilst some models of occupational choice touch on the problems of initial and subsequent job choices (Timperley's is one, see W.M. Williams, Editor Occupational Choice, 1974) no concept seems to be offered by any of them that would help to explain theoretically why 70% of doctors in this study opted for forensic pathology as a career path to follow. The data shows that these decisions were made in medical college. It would appear that they were stimulated, attracted, interested, advised, encouraged, prompted, even urged, by enthusiastic and charismatic tutors. It is (to coin a term) socialisation by 'mentoring'. This influence can occur at the induction stage, at tutelage, at lecture periods or field work, career interview, and make a formal or informal impact upon the student which permeates throughout the course. It may be transmitted on a subject basis (as a contribution to medical knowledge) or social basis (to project the detective image).

What is also clear from the evidence obtained, in contrast to the stigmatizing allusions by the non-forensic fraternity discussed earlier in this chapter (that those who enter this field are likely to be peculiar personalities or odd types) is that these discrediting suppositions or labels are quite speculative and present at best some scope for separate psychological research.

Section II. Why young doctors avoid this Specialty - A Forensic Pathologists' View.

"..career prospects poor; few full-time posts in the subject; unsocial hours;   dealing with decomposed bodies;   hanging around Courtrooms; fear of cross-examination; fear of infection (Hepatitis, Aids); poor pay; little relief cover; need to perform many autopsies; few facilities for research." (Professor K. and Dr. H.).

"...all these influences and probably many more interact and cause a series of self-destructive vicious circles...in my view, the reasons for the crisis in forensic pathology are multiple and inextricably mixed..." (Dr. L.).

Whilst the commitment of those practising is not in question, the feedback from over half the incumbents in England and Wales confirms that they are only too aware of the conditions that have accelerated the decline of the profession. Hence, the effect on recruitment continues to cause general concern. This has long alarmed the seniors and more latterly also the establishment (in this case the Home Office) which had been told that both the universities and the National Health Service (the twin sources of this advice) were no longer prepared to provide forensic pathology services as a 'by-product' of their principal activities. The general tenor of the responses from the sample of doctors has been one of exasperation and despair that this erstwhile prestigious profession has been allowed to become (what Dr. M. called) an 'orphan' one. However, following some delay and a change of chair of the PAB (Policy Advisory Board), the corner seems to have been turned and the Wasserman proposals for a unified, centrally-directed country-wide service, setting out specified conditions of work, quality control and funding, are coming to fruition at last. (Wasserman, 1989).

Blemishes related to Work.

a) Career Structure and Prospects   Appr. 14%

No proper career structure - lack of posts and prospects;
University Departments in the field are closing down;
The old part-time NHS Pathologists are not being replaced;
Government Bodies are freezing jobs;

b) Training: Appr. 11%

Undergraduate provisions for this specialty dwindling;
Students less exposed to the subject, less chance to develop an interest in it;
No training given in Court Work Behaviour;

c) Attitudes: Appr. 11%

Students are initially more clinically oriented and interested in healing;
There is an intra-professional status debasement - Forensic Pathologists are often denied the status of 'Doctor';
Students are viewed as not so dedicated these days - and also reluctant to accept the pressures placed upon Forensic Pathologists by the Police and Post Mortems;

d) Work Organisation
    (inc. Work Content and Working Conditions)   Appr. 64%

Financial Insecurity - Arbitrary Pay Structure;
Overdependence on Coroners' Work;
Shortage of Staff - little chance to spread the work which means overwork for some;
Mortuaries not centralised - thus much travelling day and night;
Large amounts of time spent in Court - often wasted;
Autopsies - history scanty or unhelpful, or often not available;
No paid holidays, sick leave or pension provided;
Little opportunity for part-time work;

No cover for those out on a case;

Not much visible research done - which normally attracts students;

Income depends on Police and Coroner who can withhold support without giving a reason;

Lack of variety in everyday work - many routine autopsies;

Stress of Cross Examination in Court - Counsel challenging one's opinion;

Mutilated Remains - autopsies very unpleasant;

A high-risk profession - Contamination of Disease;

The Self-funding nature of some departments makes for excessive bureaucratic paper work;

Forensic Pathology not a part of the NHS, hence no central direction;

Difficult to transfer from Pathology into the Forensic field.

Comments:

These brief extracts are amply elaborated in the original responses to the questions posed and make for interesting reading. It is clear that members of the whole profession were (when the questionnaires were sent out and returned) extremely unhappy with its status in society generally, and its position within the whole medical fraternity in particular. Further, the evidence suggests members to be acutely aware of the deficiencies in career prospects, recruitment and the conditions under which they are employed. A grim future for the service is predicted unless the aforementioned Wasserman proposals provide the conditions for urgent remedial action. All the answers were obtained from practising forensic pathologists who were asked to draw on their contacts, knowledge and experience to explain what are, or might be, the reasons why young doctors are reluctant to specialise in this expertise.

The self-perception of some of the respondents reveals an acute awareness that their chosen profession is tainted by stigmas. Incumbents believe that the doctors who are not forensic pathologists are critical (at times with justification) of the dubious scientific quality of some of the opinions and practices of certain members. The specialty is also rather frowned upon as inferior by Histopathologists (who specialise in the microscopical examination of tissues) involved in the training of junior pathologists whose values they may influence. In this way candidates have been known to be dissuaded from entering this field. There is a mention also of a supposed prevailing view in the community at large that working with the dead is 'infra dig'. Poor public relations (suggest some answers) can be traced to forensic pathologists from the past, who could be seen as 'publicity-seeking' individuals for whom personal aggrandisement was more important than the specialty.

Dealing with decomposed bodies, fear of infection, risk of one's reputation in Court, lack of research, bad press (see Chapters 3, 6 and Appendix 2 for case details of Helen Will, Helen Smith and Lindy Chamberlain), resentment by academics that forensic pathology has a place in a university at all (and often labelled a 'Cinderella Subject' with no academic status in the eyes of medical students), or seen as a miserable, low-morale department in the university setting, have been voiced as only some of the multiplicity of characteristics that attach stigmatizing propensities to this profession. One quote, typical of the prevailing state of morale is 'that the senior forensic pathologist in one particular city has no department, not even a secretary, and the whole service is a sort of ad hoc arrangement quite unlike other medical specialties in the National Health Service'.

It will be appreciated that the respondents answered in the light of their own experience. Thus, if only one or two complain about the absence of a provision for holidays, sickpay and pension, it does not mean that the rest is unconcerned. It merely suggests that others feel more strongly about matters to which they attach a higher priority. Dr. L. (1987), a very experienced pathologist, attended in 1988 a meeting of the Presidents of Pathology Colleges from the United States, Canada, Australia, New Zealand and South Africa. The views about the state of the discipline expressed by these leaders were somewhat different from those obtained in this country and make for an interesting comparison. Firstly, the decline of the specialty is attributed to:

a)   the lack of any modern scientific content in forensic pathology, and the fact that such advances in science that come to the fore do not seem to apply to this discipline; and

b)   the poor quality of the practitioners.

The absence of a career structure (often put forward as a reason for unsatisfactory recruitment) was discounted by the South African President because (he said) there were at least six Forensic Pathology Chairs which, on account of a dearth of suitable candidates, cannot be filled. The Australian representative expressed a similar sentiment. One assumes, however, that the reasons for the crises as voiced by these representatives will clearly be multifarious and varied, as well as relating to local conditions not necessarily similar to those in this country.

Section III. How Forensic Pathologists cope with the 'grisly' and 'polluting' work.

'*After 20,000 autopsies I still wonder, when slicing a brain, what it was thinking some hours earlier'*. (Professor N.).

'*...overtly the job has no effect on me, but I have discovered that other colleagues share with me disturbing dreams, usually of performing autopsies on my own family, when one cannot replace their organs and they are still alive!'*. (Professor N.).

'*I remember asking Professor W. how he coped with decomposed bodies. He said he had no trouble at all, except when people near him were vomiting. That made him feel nauseous'*. (Dr. V.).

This kind of work is often referred to as grisly and polluting, particularly in the media. (One good example is drawn from Sue Lawley's conversation with the late Professor Simpson on BBC1, transmitted in March, 1982).

Sue Lawley: It is thought inevitable, isn't it, that the first thing that strikes a layman, when hearing about the sort of things that you do, that he is, to some extent disgusted, revolted?

Professor Simpson: Yes, I think that's true, but he doesn't come round with me before he looks at it as a disgusting, revolting, smelly, nasty sort of job.

In conversation the Professor let it be known that he doesn't really like the word 'grisly' and that in his opinion forensic pathology is one of the most fascinating subjects that any young medical student could look at. At the age of 74 at the time, he continued to work his 'slab side' (Lawley's words), as opposed to his bed-side manner...

The question posed to the doctors in this survey refers to the effects of their work on incumbents *now* as well as to the earlier stages of their career in the field. Most of the answers concentrated on the present and those who touched on their earlier experiences simply suggested (a) that there had never been a problem, or (b) that familiarity and experience soon enabled them to make a satisfactory adjustment. Space prevents me from going into great detail here, but one or two quotations of the less usual kind may be of interest to readers. One such answer claims curiosity in anatomical dissection from an early age that started with plucking and pulling chickens at 9 years of age. Another suggested a process of natural selection whereby those who find the work offensive either never enter forensic pathology, or, if they do, soon give up. The approximate ratio between (a) and (b) is 62:38.

Coping propensities as experienced by practitioners now may be suitably categorised under three headings:

1. Interest of the Problem-solving kind,   Appr. 44%
   i.e. challenge and interest in the task outweighs the unpleasant factors, e.g.

   After following undergraduate medical education I am now well aware and mentally attuned...

   After many years working on 'grisly' cases, I do not find such scenes upsetting...

   One accepts this and gets on with the work...but I do get irritated when people give one funny looks and think I must be some sort of pervert to enjoy this work...

   At least overtly no problem...the alleged 'grisly' and odorous aspects are of no consequence as the intrinsic interest of the job far outweighs any distaste...

   The realisation that one can perform autopsies and remain physically safe by taking appropriate precautions...helps in coming to terms with this aspect; early contact with formalin-fixed anatomy specimens soon reveals whether interest is genuine...

   Now less disturbing and a challenge...I am able to switch off and not ponder over the details of each case after an autopsy...

2.   Moral and Social Value of Forensic Pathology Work   Appr. 22%

In a nutshell, you have to be able to relate your work to the welfare of the living to overcome the effects of working with the dead

I tend to have sympathy with the accused as well as compassion for the victims, however, someone has to do it - it's like emptying dustbins or cleaning sewers - a necessary social service

I think that many of us doing forensic work find (in the extreme degrees of man's inhumanity to man) this the hardest aspect to face, particularly crimes against children. However, face them we must, to establish truth and bring about justice without which the fabric of our society would crumble...

Much of forensic work is routine, yet by being observant we may save lives. Hence a triple purpose is served: detection and prevention of crime, as well as discovering a future threat of (previously undiscovered) disease. This work is an adventure of exploration...

3.   The Scientific and Professional Approach,   Appr. 33%
i.e. stressing self-control and the professional role as a scientist, e.g.

It is no problem, nor was it ever one. Pathologists are primarily scientists

...when the average person sees his first surgical operation, serious accident or attends his first autopsy, he often feels squeamish...one must assume a detached attitude to these things and 'grizzliness' is largely a word used by the lay press or novel writer. One must not become emotionally involved, and that applies to all branches of medicine.

I am too busy worrying about the scientific problems these things pose...you will find that most forensic pathologists have a well-developed sense of humour, which is very necessary if one is to preserve even the outward semblance of sanity...

*The only true risk of disease at post-mortem level is
Tuberculosis. Hepatitis B and Aids present no real threat to the
pathologist provided he practices a good technique...the so-called
grisly aspect is not noted in one's desire to be completely factual
and scientifically correct. One is thinking all the time of the
possible Courtroom in 3 to 6 months' time...*

*As a young doctor I had to examine exhumed corpses,
mangled bodies from explosion and tribal warfare...in the same
year as medical officer in charge of a famine relief camp, I saw
hundreds of people (mostly children) dying from illness and
starvation. I cannot remain indifferent to unpleasant events, but
one very quickly achieves - partly as a result of the investigative
and analytical process - an attitude of detachment which normally
means one is rarely affected*

*...one suppresses one's mental anguish in an attempt to
record the facts accurately and in detail to ensure that the
evidence presented in Court is as good as possible...*

Comments:

The frankness of these answers (of which a fuller account is recorded
in the main research) is at once commendable and revealing. After all,
these doctors let their 'professional hair' down without ever having
personally met the researcher, who, moreover, is not a person in the
medical field. There is hardly any concealment of possibly the grimmest
of any activities in a job (to an outsider, at least) that of cutting up a dead
body. Nor have most of the responses attempted any kind of ego-
protection in the sense in which the admirable Hughes (1958) used the
term 'Blinders' - meaning value-laden, collective high-status pretensions
evolving occupational groups tend to seek. Of course, the reason must
surely be that one is considering the social drama of the work and not
matters encroaching upon their specialty. The claim is that the dirty work
cannot be delegated to others, although it has been suggested that some of
it can (Wilensky, 1964). Such work is normally readily accepted as an
intimate part of the very activity which gave the incumbents of earlier
decades their charismatic public image, in contrast to the healer-doctors,
who are frequently not averse to wounding the egos of those in the
humbler hospital occupations by passing all the dirty work to them.
(Saunders, 1979).

The professional socialisation of medical students is somewhat peripheral to this study, although answers to such questions as 'what factors sparked off early interest in forensic pathology' and information concerning later decisions to specialise in the field, are not inconsistent with the researches of student physicians in America initiated by Merton (1957) in year 1952, or the study of 'Boys in White' began in 1956 under the direction of Howard Becker. Both these investigations illustrated how, during the course of becoming a doctor, ideologies tended to be subject to variations. Remarkable in this section of the responses is that some 84% have been able to cope and come to terms with this work during the earlier stages of their careers. It is probably dangerous (without further research) to claim - as some answers ventured to suggest - that this stamps them as a special breed, separate from the rest of the medical fraternity.

Doctors in general seem to regard lay people as emotional reactors to anything that relates to the human body and to assume that such people find bodily fluids disgusting and mortality frightening. By contrast, the pathologist's response is more towards coming to terms with the gruesome nature of the work, to act 'professionally', put emotions and personal feelings aside, or exercise control over them as learned in medical school. Such answers as: becoming attuned mentally; treating the activity purely as a job; seeing it as a necessary service like cleaning sewers; cultivating a detached attitude; and treating the work as an exploration on an intellectual level, could all be seen as a replacement of the cultural taboos with a modicum of rationality and emotional detachment. A good 70% from the three categories appear to take such a position, but would include also those who see the role of crime detection and prevention as a necessary social service or a contribution to the welfare of the living.

Close on 30% (in the full responses) concede that they are psychologically affected as revealed by such answers as: feeling sad about unnecessary violence; work causing distaste; distress resulting from child murder and sexual abuse; incumbent worried about own normality; mental anguish to be suppressed; sympathy with the accused; disturbed by the glee of senior colleagues; needing a sense of humour; sharing with colleagues unsettling dreams; active imagination visualising pain when death has been agonising; in heart-rending cases it is possible to do the job and still retain a real sense of pity and humanity. A small number of replies could be grouped under broader philosophical rationalisations, examples of which are: life has pleasant and unpleasant aspects; or, there are psychologically threatening elements in all branches of clinical medicine. Over and above this tentative classification from the responses, incumbents will clearly also be affected by the conditions prevailing in individual work settings and the personal impact upon their experiences and senior status.

Section IV. How doctors cope with the Dilemma of being reminded of their own Mortality.

> "A lot of the time I don't cope (have not learned how to). I developed a glib humour as a protective skin. Also, I smoke too much, drink too much, burn the candle at both ends, and do not expect to enjoy (if that's the word) a long and happy retirement. More seriously, I do not fear death - it's just that some modes of dying aren't very nice, so I shall try to choose mine in due course". (Dr. J.).

> "Once they are dead - or even terminally unconscious - I find no further interest in this aspect. To me, a body is merely a machine for transporting sentience, the latter expiring when the machine fails...as a convinced atheist, my own mortality is a matter of complete indifference to me. I am not concerned with death, only with the manner of dying...". (Professor N.).

The professional role of the respondents requires that dead bodies are handled frequently and in doing so it is likely that they are reminded of their own mortality. This may well be regarded as a kind of inbuilt dilemma with which these doctors have to learn to cope. This section identifies briefly edited responses under three distinct categories:

1. <u>Reminded or not reminded of own mortality through their work.</u>

Reminded -
> Yes, possibly the reason for choosing this career;
> One wonders about one's own 'quietus'
> I feel it more than most, I imagine; It does affect me - I burn the candle at both ends;
> These problems are not restricted to forensic pathologists;
> Yes, I am reconciled to the idea of death;
> I am well aware of death as I get older.

Not affected -

> *The work does not make me worry about death;*
> *I can remain detached, job and mortality of self are separate;*
> *Too busy to dwell on this question;*
> *I am an atheist - ludicrous to think otherwise;*
> *At heart I am a fatalist, so do not fear death.*

Reminded, by other factors than work -

> *Don't need to handle dead bodies to be reminded;*
> *It is my religious upbringing that reminds me;*
> *More potent is the increasing loss of one's friends.*

2. <u>Degrees of Coping</u>.

Coping by rational means -

> *By saturation with death in the course of work;*
> *By the 'it couldn't happen to me' approach;*
> *By simply regarding the body as a machine that fails;*
> *By enlisting religion - Christianity, Buddhism;*
> *By getting support from non-medical friends;*
> *By resorting to glib humour for protection;*
> *By keeping the psyche stable through one's way of life.*

Coping less well -

> *Death affects me, I have never learnt to cope;*
> *Forensic pathologists are prone to suicide.*

3. <u>Using philosophical (or sociological) rationalisations.</u>

> *One copes as tomorrow may never come;*
> *As a rule, the emotional interferes with the rational;*
> *The death of a colleague makes a greater impact;*
> *Some cases affect me more than others, but the job must go on;*
> *Depends on one's outlook towards horror and triumph;*
> *One learns to live with these problems;*
> *I guess a corpse hasn't much to think over;*
> *As Gabby Hayes (in the early Westerns) said: 'if the bullet's gotten your name on it, it's gonna git you!';*
> *Qualifying in forensic medicine leads to alienation from the rest of medicine.*

It is worth pointing out that those who say they have not learnt to cope are in fact coping as they are in the job and doing it. It may also be noted from the detailed responses that there is often an overlap of or justification of a contradictory feeling. For example, the professor who may regard the body as a machine with sentience expiring when that machine fails, may still have compassion, feel despair or agonise over the manner of dying in certain cases. This may be so whether he is an atheist or not.

Degrees of Coping - Approximate Percentages:

Coping by various means	63%
Employing philosophical rationality	22%
Coping less well	15%

Comments:

Once again, the candour and sincerity of these doctors is particularly striking. They do not, as they might easily have done, slide over or shirk matters that go to the very root of one's soul - their own life and death. The value of the answers is not just in the discovery of how the respondents cope with the daily reminder of their mortality, but in their attitudes towards death that are being revealed through visually encountering it on every day of their working lives. One can only express surprise that coping propensities in a psychological sense have not yet found their way into the curricula of medical education in death-related work. It has been a puzzle for some time to discover why (as some respondents have claimed) the suicide rate among pathologists is higher than that of other members of the medical profession (see A. Keith Mant, 1987, A. C. Hunt, 1987) as well as why some of the earlier charismatic leading lights in this profession committed suicide at the very end of their working lives, when it may be presumed that stress arising from it is no longer a problem. Maybe the answer to this question can be read into a clue offered by Doctor J.:

"I do not fear death - it's just that some modes of dying aren't very nice, so I shall choose mine in due course."

Intimating intention of an action actually carried out by at least four such experts in recent years (whom Professor N. said in a personal letter to this researcher he could name). The reasons for and the extent of the suicides is, however, beyond the scope of this research.

One of the respondents (Dr. V.) perceives those qualified in forensic medicine as alienated from other members in the world of medicine and posed the question how few would be willing and able to remove an appendix (from a living patient) or stop at an accident. This is topped up by other responses which suggest that the forensic pathologist's authority is merely over the body as an 'object' rather than a live person. To quote two examples: '...when your life has finished the body is left for a short time and that is that...I guess the corpse hasn't much to think over...' (Professor C.). '...if anything, my work has reassured me as I find that a dead body does not really resemble a living person'. (Dr. E.). Responses of this nature seem to deny the forensic pathologist doctor status by his own peers, who may perhaps be unaware that by following the ethos of the body as a lifeless object, they therefore (rightly or wrongly) abstract it as a 'non-patient' and so themselves as non-healers. And yet, as an interesting counter-paradigm, there are also references in the answers to mortality as a concept that affects all those practising medicine and hence 'doctor' identity. This obvious ambivalence serves us to illustrate a condition which at one and the same time symbolises what is publicly esteemed (e.g. the profession of doctor) and what is culturally offensive (e.g. manipulating dead bodies).

Section V. The Forensic Pathologist as an Expert Witness in Court.

"...we practitioners are at the moment isolated and 'one-man-bands', which is unhealthy. Also expert witnesses are often used as 'scapegoats' by lawyers when sensational events happen in Court..." (Dr. A.).

"...the facts of a case are seldom in dispute between the prosecution and the defence pathologist, but the interpretation may be. This should be resolved before the case comes to Court so as to avoid 'trial by ambush'...". (Dr. B.).

The question refers to the extreme vulnerability of the professional member when giving evidence in a Court of Law. This has indeed presented problems in the past as, on occasions, discredited opinions have harmed and even destroyed careers. Respondents were asked for their views how such a witness role might best be played. The answers divided broadly into general statements on suitable conduct in Court as well as specific, meaningful narratives or personal, and at times, stressful experiences, imposing a blemish upon the professional credibility of the incumbent concerned, which may permanently undermine both reputation and career. This Law Court question was meant to be addressed to Forensic Pathologists rather than to Forensic Scientists, although a small number of answers made references to the latter. As these two functions are often confused, it may be helpful to clarify the distinction once more before the categorisation of the responses is attempted.

FORENSIC SCIENTISTS AND FORENSIC PATHOLOGISTS -
The specialist role distinguished.

According to the Home Office Research Report 92 (HMSO, 1987), the Forensic Science Service (FSS) exists to provide impartial information about cases submitted to it involving physical evidence from scenes of crime, such as broken glass or blood-stained clothes. Staff of the FSS are not medically qualified although some, as biologists or chemists trained to degree level or beyond, carry out sophisticated analyses of human remains. These scientists do not normally deal with fingerprints, considered by and large a most clear-cut form of evidence at the scene of a crime. The FSS is not a secret organisation but has tended to adopt a low profile towards the outside world. Even some police officers (who have made use of it) feel unsure about what it can or can not do. The FSS does not produce an annual report and little has been published regarding its work.

If in a particular university (like Sheffield) the medical faculty is quite large, there may also be attached a forensic pathology arm as a separately located Medico-Legal Centre, with a coroner's office and laboratory in the same building. It may employ a wide range of people, such as senior technicians, nowadays of graduate status de facto, and other professionals, such as physiotherapists, radiographers and nurses, recognise laboratory technical work equal to and as part of the specialist services to medicine.

The work of the Forensic Pathology Service has been discussed in detail already and constitutes the main area of this research. To distinguish it briefly from the FSS, it is a small, separately organised group of doctors, called upon by the Courts to provide medical explanations of causes of death. The Brodrick Committee (HMSO, 1971) (set up to report on Death Certification and Coroners), (referred to in the previous Chapter), in its 1971 Report describes the role of the forensic pathologist (a century ago) as the principal adviser to the police and the coroner, but later uses the term 'forensic pathology' in a more restricted sense as a responsibility simply to undertake the postmortem examination of bodies found in 'suspicious circumstances' in order to establish, as far as possible, the cause of death. The Wasserman Report of 1989, which also contains this information, stresses the forensic pathologists' vital role in the criminal justice system of this country. Let us now look at the responses under three headings:

1. Critical of the System.

> *The vulnerability of the professional member (expert witness) is a direct consequence of the adversarial system;*
> *Under the present system practitioners are isolated (from professional inter-checking) and work as 'one-man-bands';*
> *I do not believe that the witness box in a Crown Court is the correct place for differences of interpretation and opinion to be debated;*
> *The scientist as an expert witness in Court is on foreign territory...it is not in the interests of the profession for experts to be seen squabbling in open Court - when they are merely being used as tools by the legal profession;*
> *Secret technical defences are now no longer allowed - I managed to start the agitation which led to Section 81 of the Police and Criminal Evidence Act, requiring scientific evidence to be declared beforehand.*

2. Opinions on how the job (of acting as an expert witness in Court) should be done.

> *The witness should expound only proven theories and not make unsound scientific observations;*
> *'To thine own self be true' - it has from time to time made me unpopular;*
> *The stress of Court work is more difficult to cope with than the intrinsic medical side of the job;*
> *If the general standard of forensic pathology were higher, room for disagreement would be much smaller;*

The forensic pathologist must be prepared (in Court) to 'put his mouth where his pen was', that is, (justify what he put into his report);

The standard of proof or the justification for an opinion is so much higher in Courts than it is in a therapeutic or diagnostic situation...;

The forensic pathologist cannot possibly be expected to keep up with the explosion of knowledge, even in his own field...;

I have always taken the view that the position is analogous to a professional boxer, no one wins them all and if you take the money, you may also have to take the stick that comes with it;

One is unfortunately not in a position to correlate wounds to any blows, as one often has to do the job without the benefit of evidence in the witness box;

Court appearances are undoubtedly the most harrowing aspect of a forensic pathologist's duties, but there are ways to minimise the anxieties...;

The eminence of one's status makes the acceptance of one's views more likely;

One problem in court is often to answer difficult scientific questions 'off the cuff';

It is often not a matter of 'true' or 'false' but weighing up probabilities.

3. Harassment or other unfair Treatment by Counsel.

Expert witnesses (such as forensic pathologists) are often used as 'scapegoats' by lawyers when sensational events happen in Court;

'Trial by Ambush' would be avoided if the interpretation of facts were to be discussed and agreed upon between the prosecution and defence witness before the case comes into Court;

It is not unusual for counsel to ignore facts which are not helpful to their case - I have now adopted a far more cynical approach to giving evidence...;

There is a general undercurrent in the profession that the forensic pathologist may himself be placed 'on trial' in the witness box to win a case for the defence...;

It is all a game for the legal profession and the barristers are no more than actors on a stage...

THE CLIFT CASE AS INDICATIVE OF LEGAL THREATS TO THE OCCUPATIONAL STATUS OF FORENSIC SCIENTISTS AND FORENSIC PATHOLOGISTS.

Dr. Alan Clift (1984), the (then) Secretary of the International Association of Forensic Sciences, advised this researcher that the unwillingness of candidates to enter this specialism has (in his view) at least partly to do with the possibility that their professional status may be undermined and damaged without an adequate opportunity to reply in defence of one's case. This undermining and damaging is done by members of other professions (such as the law) who in our society have privileged or other favoured opportunities to provide unilateral comment. Dr. Clift has been accused of simply trying to aid police by not including vital evidence on blood groupings in the case of John Preece, the lorry driver jailed for life for the murder by strangling of a woman from Aberdeen (Helen Will), but later freed (Phillips, 1983, see also Appendix 2 for details of all cases referred to in this chapter).

The lessons that emerged from this tragic case appear to be that serious consequences follow from withholding some evidence, giving opinions not backed by scientific evidence, and giving evidence that lacked accuracy and scientific detachment (on the part of Dr. Clift). Problems with the legal adversary system can also be identified: conflicting scientific evidence from expert witnesses confuses a jury, who are inclined to accept more from the one who holds himself or herself out to be an advocate of his or her cause as against that expert who is less famous but objective. Also, under the present system, the parties are at liberty to choose what expert they wish to call to give evidence, and expert witnesses are not obliged to state what their evidence does not prove, which in any case may be difficult under a question and answer system in cross examination. Further points to note are that, unwittingly, volunteering inadmissible evidence may lead to a mis-trial, whilst, additionally, neither prosecution nor defence lawyers may be clear about complex scientific evidence and reluctant to ask for clarification in the course of the trial.

One grievance of Dr. Clift was that he could not properly defend himself because Home Office employees are bound by the Official Secrets Act. No one of the (then) 87 scientists working there were able to speak publicly about the Clift case. It was known that they were angry about suggestions that his alleged faults were in fact the standards of the profession as a whole. Moreover, they were also upset by the implication that Dr. Clift was victimised (as a relative newcomer) by those who wanted his position as biology head of the section. Dr. Clift firmly believed that he was the victim of a fundamental change of attitude in the top echelons at the Home Office about the way forensic scientists should do their work. Following his training, he always believed it to be his duty as a scientist investigating crime to draw conclusions where they are justified and be prepared to tell the Court his expert opinions. But now, says Dr. Clift in a personal letter to the author, it seems experts are discouraged from giving any firm opinion to the Court. They must restrict themselves to the bare facts, even if this means dumping on to a jury a load of technical - to them probably incomprehensible - information, to make of it what they can.

A comment on the way in which a forensic scientist should do his or her work was interestingly stated (in relation to Dr. Clift) by the late Miss Margaret Pereira, then head of one of the Home Office Forensic Science laboratories, assigned to work on some of Dr. Clift's past cases. She said in a passage of her final report (as quoted by Phillips, 1983, p. 711) that...

> '...in many ways Dr. Clift's attitude reflects those of the very early forensic scientists who saw their function as helping the police and not as, I would believe, a modern forensic scientist would see it, namely to assist the police in their investigations and secondly, to assist in the cause of justice in the Courts. He does not seem to have turned his mind to the possibilities of his evidence incriminating innocent people, trusting that the police were always right in their initial suspicions'.

It will have been noted from some of the responses to Court appearances that a number of doctors have suffered from lasting psychological damage to their selves so as to mark them for the rest of their professional lives. Probability plays a large part in the reconstruction of cause of death and should forensic science prove to be fallible by evidence that later comes to light in just one single instance of a career, no matter that the expert has had years of experience and been right in hundreds of cases in the past, a career is tainted and can result in a diminished status vis-à-vis one's colleagues and/or removal from the Home Office list. The circumstances are often not in any way comparable with those of the Clift case when, for example, an experienced professor is asked to assess long after the event whether a cut in a piece of material (in this case the garment worn by a child) amounts to homicide. This has occurred in the 'Dingo Baby' case 1980, (Lexis Printouts, 1983/4), which shows how matters can take a wrong turn when (for whatever reason) the surrounding social factors are not taken into account by those interpreting what can be gleaned from a case.

The survey answers from the doctors, together with the Clift and Chamberlain cases, clearly show why it is that the majority (some 74%) expressed much apprehension at an appearance as expert witness in Court. On one question of survival in the legal jungle, Professor Gee (1988) in his paper to the BAFM has said that the forensic pathologist has almost no training for that role and how difficult it is to get experience in advance of actual exposure in cross examination during a major case. There are often changes in Court procedure and the medical profession does not take enough notice of the needs of lawyers and the Courts. There is a need for formal training in witness techniques, especially in the light of changing attitudes towards expert witness evidence. The doctors who say they have no fear and cope confidently (some 10%) are in the main senior people who by reason of their personal disposition, good preparation (frequently obtained by study for additional, legal qualifications) and years of exposure, have most likely been fortunate enough not to have encountered an extraordinarily difficult case or bullying Counsel attempting to discredit their evidence in a public domain and fracture their ego permanently, as well as damage the status and public image of forensic pathology as a profession.

Section VI. Probing the Public Image of Pathologists in Forensic Medicine.

"*At the present time, the Royal College of Pathologists, in its Silver Jubilee year, is spending a small fortune employing a firm of PR experts to try to foster its public image...I think it will be money down the drain as public attention is totally fickle and evanescent...*" (Professor N.).

"*In many ways, the inconsistent public image matters less than the image held by the medical and legal professions. But to answer the question, the public image is, first of all, confused. Forensic Pathologists, Police Surgeons, Forensic Scientists, are all lumped together like an interesting stew, with good bits and not so good bits...*" (Dr. F.).

In this final section respondents were asked to say what factors, in their opinion, affect the public image of their profession and how they view this image at the present time. The raw responses from the doctors, written in qualitative terms onto the answer sheets, are accompanied by a good deal of *obiter dicta* and are presented here (in a slightly trimmed down version). Two main categories of answers emerged to project, on the one hand, adverse indicators and, on the other, characteristics seen as favourable. A very small number of the responses (some 12%), not perhaps warranting a separate classification, opted for statements with a more neutral flavour, suggesting that the profession's public image is shaped by a mixture of influences and that this image can vary in accordance with media representations that happen to be of current interest, whether this be a press report of a court case (e.g. Dr. Clift), film (the Dingo Baby Case) or Home Office Report, obtainable from HMSO (e.g. the Wasserman Report).

1. Adverse Indicators.

> *My opinion is affected not only by my professional work and reading the press, but also in social contacts: 'Oh how revolting, how could you work with dead bodies, doesn't is smell awful'; or 'Don't you think the pathologists have made fools of themselves in the Dingo Baby case?".*

> *Public image of forensic pathology is conditioned by ignorance of the job and by such television programmes as 'Quincy', 'The Expert', etc., which often bear little resemblance to reality. My wife's nursing colleagues have a very bizarre idea of what I do: 'He cuts up people for the Police.'.*

> *The old days when Spilsbury, Simpson and Camps were household names have gone. The public is too overwhelmed with the tidal wave of the media so that, except for passing excitement when some gruesome multiple or sex murder comes along, they are too concerned with Page 3 of the Sun and sports news to care about pathologists.*

> *If Royalty were assassinated and they couldn't find a decent forensic pathologist to help in the investigation, then for a couple of days the public may notice us (e.g. Dallas); but short of that, we are a non-starter in terms of public interest.*

The profession is regarded by some in a poor light. Media coverage is mainly to blame. The press and television have recently got into a vendetta against wrongful conviction... casting serious doubts about the evidence given in some cases.

At the moment, the universities wish to see the back of us, the police accept any pathologist they can get hold of...the public do not know much about us and their need of doctors in the Courts has led them to an unflattering image about us.

To my mind, when two experts totally disagree about either the facts or the interpretation of them, it is most harmful as it raises the image that one or the other, (or perhaps both), is bending the evidence to suit the side he appears for.

2.   Favourable Indicators.

I hopefully believe that our public image at the present time is good...the public looks for the competent expert who will give an unbiased opinion and exudes honesty...

The lay public image of forensic pathology at the moment is probably good...but the image of the profession in the eyes of the medical world is low and probably still sinking...

Forensic pathology retains a good image in the eyes of the public who are interested...I have encountered nothing but respect for the position I hold...

I have no doubt that the profession is highly regarded...I am often called upon to speak to a range of lay audiences and the resultant discussion as well as the reaction from friends leaves me convinced that this is so...

The present image of forensic pathologists in the eyes of the public is reasonable...but they are not thought to be imbued with God-like qualities ascribed to some of their predecessors...

Some television series of romantic portrayals present the forensic pathologist as too clever or an oddity...

The image of forensic pathologists is still riding high on the reputation of such personalities as the late Professors Simpson and even Spilsbury...

The Home Office will now allow its pathologists in certain circumstances to act for the defence. Prior to this, the police divided them into two great camps - those on the List were always believed to be extremely honest and competent...

Comment:

There is little doubt from the bulk of the full and sincere responses that an approximate 78% assess realistically the great concern members feel about how the image of the profession is being evaluated. As shown earlier, in some cases (e.g. Clift, Chamberlain, Arthur and Helen Smith, or more latterly, the Louise Woodward case in the States and the murder of the nurse in Saudi, even the current demand by the family of Hanratty to exhume his body, see Appendix 2 for all case details) there may be mistaken professional attitudes about the way the work should be done; disagreements on the interpretation of evidence between prosecution and defence experts; impaired credibility when privileged information is not disclosed, or medical facts known to one side only and sprung suddenly upon the other in court; risks to reputation in genuine mistakes when inferring from exhibits what has occurred; or when scientific laboratory findings turn out to be fallible; and when exhibits cause colleagues totally to disagree. Neither, of course, is occupational image enhanced when the term 'bent' pathologist is used or legitimate fears about the less qualified expressed. Also given that the public image is confused by incongruous media presentation, the image problem is compounded by the antagonism of the wider medical fraternity, namely the clinicians, who tend to deny the so-called 'cadaveric' group the esteemed status of 'healer'. However it has been found that in the eyes of some forensic pathologists at least, their work is much to be preferred to the 'living death' of general practice as undertaken by most GP's in the country - 'no risk, no responsibility, no pleasure!'.

The detailed qualitative evidence obtained suggests that the various segments of the central proposition as stated at the end of Chapter 5 (status ambiguity, occupational stigmatisation, ambivalent identity, law court traumas and unsocial demands on time) has been substantially verified by the large majority surveyed and the negative perception of their social location within the profession of medicine confirmed. Whilst some of these stigmatising tendencies have come strongly to the fore, there are (as found in other previously investigated death-related occupations, funeral directors, embalmers and grave diggers), also counter forces operating to lesson the adverse status position as the sample doctors perceive it. Even so, it would appear as the latent and manifest catalogue of stigmas presented at the end of this chapter show, that the profession has not yet achieved the favourable public recognition it possibly deserves.

Forensic Pathologists as Types.

An attempt at a typology of this professional group proves somewhat speculative, but this provides a useful tool for linking the empirical findings to a higher order of classification that takes chronological age at particular points of time in a career progression into account. It also distinguishes two principal pathways, those of 'town' and 'gown', of significance in the roads embarked upon between hospital and university. But before presenting these, it is as well to point out that the small number of professors in the country (some 10 and reducing through retirement) constitute the formal elite, although a lack of departmental research or discredit in a court (and the resulting publicity) at some stage, in the working life of the doctor, could endanger personal prestige.

Sociologists have attempted career typologies in the past. The Americans Miller and Form selected some classifications which could be suitably applied to personal work histories in which social class is distinguished: the climbers (slow and steady progress); the Brahmins (probably starting at the top and staying there); the skidders (whose class position steadily deteriorates); the proletariat (whose total work career is at a low level); and the irregulars (who shift from one level to another). (Miller & Form, 1964). Another, more general classification is that used by Hughes (1958, p.129) to differentiate career patterns between the 'itinerants', who believe in moving from place to place for progress; and the 'home-guard', who choose to operate in a narrower orbit or remain loyal to one particular institution. Found in the survey of this research are the doctors that to Hughes are the 'true missionaries', sectarians who have no judge except God himself. The number of those committed to this belief is, however, small.

In his discussion of what makes a 'physician', Hughes identified three components which typify an ideal patient: amenability to treatment, a good interactive relationship, and a beneficial influence on the doctor's career. This leads one to wonder about an 'ideal autopsy', on which no view has been expressed by the respondents, other than the desirability of a clean and efficiently-run mortuary. One young pathologist's survey response identified three typical doctors located in the public mind, as already discussed earlier on page 4: the formally attired Bernard Spilsbury of world fame; the Quincy-like technologist, whose ranting and raving alone could wake the dead; and the accurate BBC portrayal of a pathologist's work by actor Marius Goring during the 1980s, who himself spent hours researching the part at Guy's Hospital.

Comments:

The 20-year old Quincy programmes retained their popularity and enjoy frequent repetition. One recalls also Goring's part as Dr. Hardy, the forensic scientist, helping Chief Inspector Fleming solve complex murders in 'The Expert' TV series. Incidentally, Professor Glaister of Glasgow University (an uncle of the producer) served as role model in these dramas. Page 4 refers also to the 'Gladsone Murder Bag', which formed the central theme in an ITV presentation featuring the esteemed Superintendent Lockhart. The briefcase-like bag, containing 80 items of equipment to compile evidence at the scene, later became standard police kit everywhere. There have been a number of television forerunners to 'The Expert', of course. One such was 'The Hidden Truth', (ITV 1964), where the leading personality, that of Professor Robert Lazard, at work on crimes such as arson and insurance fraud, prescribed a strict maxim for his team: 'Stay clear of involvement', which meant no discussion - even among the members themselves - of the cases they were handling. That has not been found to be the actual practice in a team situation now, as Chapter 7 will show, when colleagues may well discuss or exchange views on a case. As far as current media presentations of the work of forensic pathologists are concerned (e.g. 'Mc Callum' ITV and 'Silent Witness' BBC1 the most recent), the profession is generally not highly pleased and indeed drives one Professor frantic. He does not know of a single pathologist who has time for these unrealistic programmes. The reality is that forensic pathologists do in no circumstances interfere with the work of the police or the clinical aspects of investigation of a suspicious death. Quite a number of the doctors are frequently consulted by television producers and advice is given on how forensic pathologists work, but that advice is repeatedly ignored.

Careers and Qualifications.

Returning now to the problems of qualifying as an 'expert' in forensic medicine, the general view expressed by leading members of the profession (Green, 1974, 1998, Wecht, 1977, Cameron, 1980, Knight, 1985, Mant, 1986) was until very recently (1998) that there is no proper career structure. The information obtained from Dr. Kellett (1986), who is a Consultant Histopathologist and Home Office Pathologist, is that of two distinct ways in which a newly-qualified doctor can set off on a career in forensic pathology: he or she can try to get into an academic department of forensic medicine and work up the ladder, or take up a career in histopathology (specialising in the microscopical examination of tissues) in the National Health Service and be based in a hospital, become experienced in forensic medicine, and then apply to become a Home Office Pathologist. The two schemes are shown below.

Career Path in Forensic Pathology.

(The two schemes assume that the medical qualification has been obtained at the approximate age of, say, 24 years).

Scheme A.

House Jobs (at 26)
Academic Medical Department
MRC(Path) Examination
plus
DMJ(Path) Examination
plus
Experience
Home Office Recognition

Academic Forensic Pathologist (34)

Scheme B.

House Jobs (at 26)
N.H.S. Based
MCR (Path) Examination
plus
Experience
N.H.S. Consultant (36)
DMJ(Path) Examination
plus
Experience
Home Office Recognition

Part-time Home Office Pathologist (40)

Drawbacks in Scheme A.
There are very few training posts in forensic pathology outside London. These have to be University-based, and if the MRC (Path) examination is taken in forensic pathology, it qualifies the holder only to

practice forensic medicine. As the job opportunities are so few, this may lead to a dead-end in career prospects.

Drawbacks in Scheme B.

Most of the histopathy consultants in the N.H.S. have no experience, or indeed interest, in forensic pathology. If one has an interest, the applicant must either approach, or be approached by such authorities as the Police, the Coroner, or even the Home Office itself. Having once gained the necessary experience and qualifications, he or she may then practise as a part-time Home Office Pathologist provided a post is vacant within the region, and the Home Office gives recognition to the post.

Additional Problems with Scheme B.

Dr. Kellet (1986) stresses (i) the difficulty for an N.H.S.-based pathologist to obtain the necessary experience and training in homicide cases, essential to perform the work and, at the same time, take the DMJ examination; (ii) furthermore, such pathologists experience hostility from their N.H.S. colleagues, who dislike to cover for them when they are absent from work, either on a case or acting as witness in Court; (iii) some employing authorities do on occasion demand that the N.H.S.-based forensic pathologist must switch to part-time work in his/her N.H.S. post, resulting in a significant drop in salary as well as pension entitlements, merit awards and other possible financial benefits.

Proneness to Suicide - An additional Hazard.

Section IV in this chapter has already touched on the nature of this specialised work and the ways in which it serves to remind a doctor of his own mortality. The higher than average suicide rate among forensic pathologists has yet to be further researched, in particular why it is that this occurs at times at the end of a working life, when one would assume the elements of stress no longer to be there. One of the respondents pointed to a possible clue that, having had to deal with modes of dying which are 'not very nice', he will choose his own departure when the time is right. Dr. L. (a very senior member of the profession, who has assisted with evidence for the Wasserman Report) writes in response to a survey follow-up question that he is aware of five suicides among members of the profession during the last couple of decades (apart from the famous Professor Spilsbury, who gassed himself in his laboratory as mentioned (page 53) on the eve of his retirement), among them a Glasgow Professor and two doctors, one of whom took his own life by an overdose of drugs and the other by hanging. Dr. Sakinofsky, from the

Institute of Psychiatry, published brief research findings on the 'Suicide of Doctors and their Wives' and established in the case of male doctors that it amounts to thrice the rate of the general public, ten times that of Members of Parliament and senior civil servants, and six times that of university teachers and the clergy. Two controversial reasons are suggested in this article: (a) that the special knowledge of toxicology and surface anatomy doctors have may mean that impulsive suicide attempts are usually more fatal than those attempted by the public generally; and (b) that the stresses related to the practice of medicine may possibly interact with personality flaws in vulnerable doctors, and so play a part. (Sakinofsky, 1980). An incidence of suicide in later life has also been discovered among holocaust survivors, attributable (at least in part) to the guilt and torment of being alive when others had to die. This research is still in its infancy but has also relevance to survivors of disasters who then need counselling and psychotherapy treatment for possible relief. (Ashurst, 1989). The name given to this recently recognised condition is 'Post Traumatic Stress Disorder', and might afford an additional clue to explaining the suicides of the forensic pathologists.

Science and Law in Forensic Work - Is it a Marriage of Opposites?

If a professional member in this field wants to avoid the influence of lawyers, court appearances and crime scenes, all he or she needs to do is to become isolated in a laboratory. A good many have chosen to do that and so contributed to break-throughs in medicine by handling compounds or devising formulae and solutions which help to enhance (and sometimes may be harm) the quality of our lives, although scientists in this position have probably never seen a patient or handled a corpse. Such contributions as are made in the laboratory do not invalidate earlier findings but build on them and achieve a continuation of scientific progress in this way. Moreover, argues Anita Ky Wonder (1989), that is precisely why progress in forensic science is being impeded by the criminal justice system. Whereas science continues to change (or ceases to be science), the law rarely changes, for, if it did, it would cease to be law. It is because the courts and large doses of the law are at the final stage in the application of forensic science, that demands are continually placed on laboratories to adapt to a legal philosophy. It just is not possible to acquiesce completely, says Ky Wonder.

Whilst scientists testify within the ambit of their changing discipline, the lawyers want solid, unshakable answers and an adherence to precedents. But some scientists prefer to take an inflexible stance and adhere to basic premises long refuted by later knowledge and so can, as independent experts, earn a good deal of extra income from their appearance in Court. The majority, however, do feel branded if they are not allowed to take account of acquired knowledge, change or modification and therefore make an active contribution in evidence to forensic science. Ky Wonder does not suggest that scientists become lawyers or the reverse, but wants the two disciplines to compromise on both roles and philosophies, in cases where forensic evidence is introduced and also in meetings to establish a freedom to disagree if injustices and stifled development are not to result. Forensic science, she feels, needs a good parental relationship in this marriage or the offspring will be denied future success. This sentiment certainly invites sympathy but one also recalls that an Australian scientist, connected with the Dingo Baby case, failed to adhere to the manufacturer's instructions for handling a substance in the laboratory test, which resulted in a confusion of copper dust with human blood and the (temporary) conviction of Lindy Chamberlain - a case of human error in science misleading the law. Or as Dunn (1981) informs us - technical rationality is one thing and legal rationality another, requiring to reconcile the reasoned choices of the former with the legal conformity of the latter.

Rationality, Probability and Certainty.

There are standards of routine and behaviour which a forensic pathologist adopts when he or she is confronted by a corpse. Garfinkel calls these descriptions of conduct 'rationalities', to include on the part of the incumbents as scientists feelings of 'affective neutrality' - being detached, unemotional, disinterested, impersonal. He also holds that there occur tolerable errors when assessing the degree of fit between what is observed by a person and what that same person intends as his or her findings. What errors are tolerable in forensic work may well become intolerable later, as we have seen. Garfinkel applies rationality to coroners who must try to construct from the evidence a recognisable rational account of the course of events which produced the body of the deceased as its end result. (Garfinkel, 1974, 1967). One could argue that there are in any evaluation degrees of scientific credibility which will consist of one or more of three different kinds of certainty: one that is similar to mathematical probability, deducible from a relationship between a known proposition and an other that may not be; another may be an inference from what has been observed and from which an abstract model may be constructed; the third kind relates to a credibility which is not capable of numeration but can be subjectively adjudged by way of a scale or continuum. Whereas the scientist in evidence will wish to have regard to the first two, the forensic pathologist (who incidentally also regards himself or herself as a scientist) will often be faced with the third in an attempt to opine from visual clues action to which he or she was not a witness. In Court an expert's opinion is usually scrutinised whether or not it agrees with that of another expert, but the dilemma of degrees of credibility has not yet been solved.

CONCLUDING OBSERVATIONS:

It is now possible, from all the accumulated evidence in the preceding chapters, to present in summary form the actual and potential stigmatising propensities that attach to the profession of forensic pathology. Past fortunes in evolution and the weight of the responses by members practising this specialty today would seem to support the proposition contained in the hypothesis (see Chapter 5) that a stigma is present, although a number of vital status-enhancing characteristics have come to the fore to press for recognition and these have also been identified below.

Stigmatising Propensities

The stigmatising propensities of forensic pathology are as follows:-

the profession's unattractive image given it by medical students and other specialists in medicine; an apparent denial by other members of the medical fraternity that forensic pathologists are 'doctors' or 'healers'; accusations of character blemishes and allusions to 'bent' pathologists; stigmas relating to peculiarities of personality; and also those originating in the courts from discredited evidence for what ever reason; stigmas associated with the nature of 'death work' itself - handling dead bodies and performing autopsies; stigmas of recognition of the subject's importance in universities and the establishments; the lack of this recognition affecting working conditions (shortages, anomalies in the pay structure, a poor working environment, few research facilities or opportunities); stigma of evaluation of the discipline itself - frowned upon as inferior and lacking scientific validity or quality; threat of disunity in the profession between town and gown, as well as between the laboratory specialist and the 'field worker' - antagonism arising from an informal dictum that the former 'police' the latter; the fragmentation arising from private and public service tends to create a disunity in the profession; and finally the press and other media have in the past (and may do so in the future if the opportunity presents itself) projected the profession in an unfavourable light.

Status Enhancing Characteristics.

Forensic Pathologists are doctors after all and have gone through the same rigorous training as other doctors, in addition to obtaining specialist qualifications in Pathology and Medical Jurisprudence.

The Wasserman Report (1989) of the Working Party on Forensic Pathology has recognised the key role this specialty plays in our criminal justice system, and there is every hope that the review of the (until recently unsatisfactory) arrangements will result in such reorganisation of the service as is to its benefit. The very latest information from the Home Office Policy Advisory Board (February 1998) is that a new Chairman has been appointed and that the various Subcommittees are making good progress with their work in the fields of research (where annual invitations to apply for funds attract a high level of interest), accreditation and quality assurance. The Home Office itself will continue to provide financial support for senior academic posts in departments of forensic medicine and has also now instituted a series of training posts to encourage younger doctors to opt for this specialism.

In the main, respondents have adjusted well to this kind of work and say they find it no more grisly than do doctors in other branches of medicine, surgery or pathology.

Forensic pathologists, the so-called 'detectives of death', practise the art and science of making the dead body speak through the medico-legal autopsy because the patient cannot otherwise tell the expert how he/she died.

Although often regarded as the 'stepchildren of the medical profession', these doctors frequently observe things that others do not see. Battered children or drunk driving is frequently an underlying cause of unnatural death. The forensic pathologist's findings can prevent further such deaths just as other doctors can prevent disease.

Not all techniques need be confined to the dead. The clinical forensic pathologist (more common in the USA) may identify new diseases like AIDS, before they turn into an epidemic.

In major disasters or accidents, the forensic pathologist plays a key role in helping to establish the identities of dead persons from their organs on the basis of medical records and/or autopsies to reveal dangerous designs or equipment.

No definite identifiable ideology has come to light on a distinct social attitude towards forensic pathology work, but the sentiment expressed by one of the respondents could well reflect that of colleagues in the field: 'All doctors have a duty to humanity and society. Rather a body past suffering and an object of detecting the criminal before he can cause such suffering again, than no patient at all!'.

The above identified stigmatising characteristics which emerged from the survey responses and quoted extracts from discussion in professional journals have led to a consideration of derived ideas. For example, the label from other medical people that forensic pathology is too 'marginal a specialty' to choose for anyone's life's work is unfairly nailed on those who, peculiarly to them, seem disaffected by 'proper' medicine, or (according to Rose, 1965) have some kind of 'divided conscience' after internalising conflicting values. Pathologists have the problem of wanting to pass as doctors most of the time, but have obvious difficulties in how to adjust ideologically to not being healers. As a collective, the profession is too small in number to make an impact as an interest group. Although there is a Royal College of Pathologists, it represents also other groups allied to this specialty. There is also the more specialised British Association in Forensic Medicine, an organised body for those practising forensic pathology and its aims include the advancement of the study and practice of the discipline as well as to act as a negotiating and advisory body when required. It keeps a register of fellows and members but does not itself publish a journal. It has little clout as a pressure group or its influence would long ago have halted the profession's downward progression.

That the work itself is stressful has not been denied and a number of responses pointed at the proneness to suicide. Those in the know are also aware of the trend towards a two-dimensional fragmentation, firstly into groups for private hire and those in public service; and secondly into the division of such sub-specialisms as psychiatry, anthropology and the use of new scientific methods by other experts than forensic pathologists - genetic finger-printing, electronic sound analysis, the now much used facial identification techniques, computerised mathematics, sophisticated toxicology, laser microscopical techniques, gas chromatography, advances in ballistics and such (to assist forensic scientists to distinguish between striae from safe-breaking and those from bullets), stomach contents, lasers burning small craters into metal to then analyse the given-off vapour, chromatography for testing materials where arson is suspected, Polaroid cameras now used by most police surgeons, dactyloscopic finger-printing and much progress in forensic odontology). As juries have become more reluctant to convict on the evidence of police officers alone, scientific evidence has gained in importance, although it is not infallible as has been shown in the Dingo Baby case. The enormous impact of scientific progress in the detection of crime and its diversity have meant that the forensic pathologist's territory of work is considerably reduced (insofar as parts of it have not also been sloughed off as dirty work to the less-qualified, to use Wilensky's words in 1964) as he or she has to rely on the help of many other specialties in performing his/her role.

CHAPTER 7

THE POSITION OF MEDICAL DETECTIVES IN THE UNIVERSITIES AND THE NHS - AN ANALYSIS OF THE CURRENT STATE OF PLAY

If one asks why so little has been written about the development and the future of this nationally so important profession during the last 4 to 5 years, authoritative opinion has it that there is a sense of despair among the remaining seniors, who have almost given up the struggle for a brighter future. To appreciate why that is so, one needs to focus geographically on country-wide central locations to glean a picture of how the service is (inadequately) covered.

Recent information from within the profession reveals that in London's Guy's Hospital the middle-aged head may retire on health grounds with two other doctors departing to set up an independent unit at St. George's. This situation leaves London University with a mere five credible members to service the Metropolitan Police and police forces in England's South East, in effect considered too small to provide cover. London has also a Medico-Legal Centre staffed by three doctors and hoping for a possible increase of one, which may then become the largest credible group in London and the South East. Leaders of the profession are now aware that some of the police forces around London, as for example in Kent and Surrey have started to use part-time Hospital Pathologists again - a retrograde step (it is feared) in quality terms, to set the profession back into the 1960s. Cardiff-based University of Wales College of Medicine has lost its prominent Forensic Pathology Professor by retirement and there is now concern about the 'routinability' as opposed to the 'researchability' of the man tipped to take his place. It seems there are no plans to replace the Professor anyway, so Cardiff would be one doctor short. Another problem is the Police apparently considering not using the person who will be the Head of Department. If that turns out to be so, Cardiff is not going to be the credible force that it was before.

In the West Midlands, taking in Birmingham City and all the conurbations around it, there is just one part-time Health Service

Pathologist and one totally independent practitioner who earns most of his living from Coroner's Post-Mortems. As to the East Midlands at this time, one part-time doctor from Leicester, another from the Papworth Hospital in Cambridge and one from Great Yarmouth, all hospital-based, perform forensic pathology work as a profitable sideline. This leaves just Sheffield as the only stand-alone credible academic department, but with the Professor there nearing retirement and his Senior Lecturer seriously ill. Given the worst and these two most senior members becoming unavailable, can the Department be sustained? What about the situation in the rest of England and Wales? At Liverpool, the Chair in Forensic Medicine ceased in 1938, but the School of Medicine has a Sub-Department of Forensic Pathology with competent Senior staff providing expertise and opportunities for research. In contrast to Merseyside itself, Manchester is served by two doctors who have no affiliation whatever to either University or Hospital. They contract out ancillary investigations such as microscopy and toxicology, and one might ask whether the money side is a prime consideration. The incumbent at Preston, covering the North of Lancashire and Cumbria, retires in two years' time. Adverts by the Hospital for a consultant, stressing 'an interest in Forensic Pathology' as a Home Office appointment, have gone in but such appointments are not in the gift of the Trust and must have Home Office approval. Newcastle has one full-time University doctor and two part-time Hospital employees which just about meets its needs.

Just over 40 doctors are now on the coveted Home Office List in England and Wales and there is a budget of less than one million pounds per year to spend on forensic pathology services for a population of 50 million. Scotland, as a separate entity and following the recommendations of the McClusky-Bowen Report (some 5 years before Wasserman), has all of 4 million pounds a year for Forensic Pathology and Science Services to spend on just a tenth of the population. Northern Ireland is equally well served by its Office in the money stakes and is possibly over-doctored for its needs, particularly if the 'troubles' cease from troubling. The present setup gives serious concern to serving police officers and the few older members of the profession. The cost-conscious financial managers of the police seem to believe that cheap is best and have taken to using independent practitioners. On this basis, the latter competes easily with a university department like Sheffield, for example. One could draw an analogy here with running a fire brigade: the fire engine has to be paid for and the firemen's' pay found even when there is no fire and the men sit by their engine playing cards (or in the forensic field, no murders to do), whereas independent doctors can sit at home, word-process their reports and get the local BUPA hospital to see to the odd microscopical work for them. In this way they could do cases for the local police at about 750 pounds each as compared to the 1000 pounds that the Department needs to charge to keep it viable. Hence the growth in contracting out. Nor does the university itself help matters because the amount it contributes towards teaching and research is at best minimal. It is thus almost the whole of incumbents' earnings from the police alone that have effectively to cover their salaries and maintenance costs. Indeed, the Professor concerned had to convince the six Police Forces that the Department's service is worth what it charges although cowboys do exist who try to lobby the Force that they can do it for less. So far, the Police have agreed with the Professor, whose standard reply is 'if you pay peanuts you get monkeys'.

To illustrate, let us look at the situation across the Pennines. There are two people (one of whom is based in Manchester) who can carry out a major investigation, including a scene, for approximately 40 per cent of what it costs the Professor from Liverpool University, with all his ancillary expenses, technicians' salaries and so on, which is why the Greater Manchester Police in particular will use the two Independents and not the Professor. This is where Wasserman's costings went wrong. The Touche Ross accountants who compiled them based their calculations on university departments, with all the overheads of running a service 365 days a year. Hence, Wasserman recommended that at 1988 prices a case should be worth about 1000 pounds, now more after allowing for inflation. To the Independents, this is not far short of a licence to print money. A number of young doctors previously disaffected with their university and Health Service posts, have taken to working from home for the full fee and no overheads, quite forgetting that they are making no provision for retirement. It is clear that schemes providing for sickness and superannuation are infinitely superior to what the private market can offer which is why incumbency in an institutional post such as the NHS or University is the more prudent step for the young doctor to take.

In an interview, one prominent professor demonstrates by way of an example from his own department how, what is discussed above, can have an increasingly serious effect on staffing in the medium term. When he arrived at his new university appointment with a certain financial package in hand, the Medico-Legal Department (just as also planned in Leeds) was about to be marked out for closure. Stating his case, the professor pointed to the 120 suspicious deaths and to the 50 homicides a year from which could be generated an income of X-hundred thousand pounds, to pay for a number of medical staff plus secretarial and ancillary support. The position at that time was that the department was already coping annually with nearly 100 homicides and well over 200 suspicious deaths, just manageable with existing staff, but with lines of communication so long and the incidental expenses so high (having regard to the now stricter burden of proof) that an extra senior lecturer was essential. That is still the position though unaffordable at present, unless the homicide rate goes up to 130 or 140 a year. There will therefore be understaffing until the work load and income rise to that level. The young doctors particularly that have broken away seem to think that the money in their pockets is worth having. But, one must also be mindful that postings within universities no longer exceed five years duration and that such terminal appointments offer the younger professional no long-term security, so that he or she might as well choose employment in the private sector. The old concept of job security for life is also vanishing from the Hospitals with their Independent cost-conscious Trusts. The last thing they want is someone on their payroll who disappears for days on end to give evidence in Crown Court or High Court. That is why part-timers practising forensic pathology are not the flavour of the month.

We shall come to look now at Trust Status in the light of fragmentation in the National Health Service. The Professor interviewed for this study has had to fight for four years to get Honorary Consultant contracts for himself and the members of his staff. They used to hold contracts with the Regional Health Authority but since the latter were abolished and replaced (in this instance) by the Central University Hospital Trust in that area, its response was 'why should we give him an honorary contract when he does only 5 per cent of his work for our city and 95 per cent in other districts and towns'. Taking that stance by the Trust once more damages employment security and moreover means that salaries and subsidies for trainees can no longer come from a region that does not exist. One can appreciate, therefore, that the major hospital in town does not see why it should help the Professor pay the salary of a young doctor who spends most of his or her time working for police forces elsewhere in the country; and one can understand why the disappearance of the regional tier of the NHS has presented problems for Forensic Pathology.

There is one further important point to make concerning the attitudes of the Department of Health and the Home Office, which administers the Police and the Colonial Services. The former, interpreting the 1948 NHS Act strictly, has no interest in patients once they are dead and therefore needs to make no provision for either training or services directed towards investigations of sudden death in the community. Apparently, the

Home Office believes that any Hospital Pathologist can do routine Coroners' autopsies as most homicide autopsies are simple and straight-forward anyway, which obviates the need for specialist forensic pathologists. Why not go back to the 1930s and just have a couple of super specialists for the entire country, who can be called in when cases become exceptionally difficult (asks the professor)? To him it is like playing the bran tub at a party. One never knows whether a case is going to be of exceptional difficulty until one has one's hands inside it and by that time one has destroyed all the evidence that the super specialist would be looking for when he comes along.

FRAGMENTATION OF THE PROFESSION

Following attempts at implementing what the Wasserman report recommended (that is, Accreditation, Quality Assurance and Training/Research), there has been evident a disturbing trend in the profession - namely that of fragmentation. This has taken the form of 'freelancing', pathologists breaking free from both University and NHS Departments to operate as self-employed expert available on hire. It will be clear that this trend not only makes internal and external quality assurance difficult, but could also have a bearing on the number and quality of ancillary investigations which these practitioners carry out. Three aspects need to be focused upon here: the approximate percentage that has broken free; how these freelancers obtain and cover the costs of the support services they need; and how quality control is maintained.

a)   To illustrate the first, the man employed in the South West of England by the County Police is on the lowest hospital scale of pay, out of which he has to find all his expenses. Our respondent Professor sees him as a ragged-trousered philanthropist working under price and rather disapproves of it. The two up North work on a fee-per-service basis, but make most of their money from routine 'coroner-sudden-death-in-the-Community' type autopsies. Then there is the (so-called) Gang of Four at an independent Medico-Legal Centre in the Capital, which only survives because they do some 4000 routine coroners' autopsies a year (that is as many as 10 to 14 per day), although expert opinion would question whether anyone can do that number of post-mortems properly. Where these are badly done, bodies may have been opened by technicians, with pathologists giving just a cursory glance at the organs and coroners seemingly willing to pay up for this work. Similar arrangements are said to exist in other parts of the country as well. Of the 40 or so Home Office Pathologists who are independent, about 12 (approximately 15%), are so totally; a further 60% it is suspected are Hospital Pathologists, with an interest in 'freelancing' leaving a declining minority of full-timers, like our Professor.

Since Wasserman's recommendations that clients (such as the Police, Coroners and Crown Prosecution Service and at times Private Solicitors for the Defence) meet the full cost of the service, the Home Office contributes nothing, keeping merely a Register of Accreditation, imposing some form of Quality Assurance and rules on Discipline. As already mentioned there is also an Advisory Board for the profession to be maintained, but the cost of that is small compared with the old Home Office retainer, leaving the Police to pick up the bills. The Universities are no longer clients now. The only two in the country running a lecture course in Forensic Pathology and Medicine do not examine at undergraduate level. The very existence of the profession within universities is being questioned by some academics on faculty, who would be quite happy to inherit our Professor's teaching space in the curriculum, but they do not bring in 500,000 pounds a year for the University like he does, so the Dean and his Board are not disposed to kill the goose that lays the golden egg. Repeated representations to the General Medical Council over the last 20 years, stressing the importance of including Forensic Medicine, Medical Law and Medical Ethics in the undergraduate course, were answered with the plea that there is an over-full programme already and these areas can be covered at postgraduate level as a part of general professional training. The Professor we interviewed does not share this view: 'what about a newly appointed doctor in a pre-registration post who finds himself in difficulties with relatives over consent, confidentiality or completion of a death certificate?', he asks. But this is only a small voice in the wilderness.

b) Turning now to the second question, how the independents obtain laboratory backup and the facilities for the performance of autopsies, reliable opinion has it that they take as little Histology (see Note 1) as possible because more spent on investigation means less in their pockets. They take the absolute minimum and enlist such private hospitals as the Nuffield or AMI to get the sections cut there; and, toxicology is always contracted out. Even a Medico-Legal Centre may find it more economical to enlist local hospital help for limited amounts so as to render the service more unit-cost effective. Touching now briefly on the problem of research, no one - not even the Home Office - seems willing to fund research into death and dying and the forensic aspects thereof. The Ministry of Defence used to give some support but that ceased with the collapse of the Berlin Wall and the break-up of the USSR. To quote the Professor again: '...as for most of my colleagues, their attitude to research is rather similar to Herman Goering's - hearing the word 'culture' made him reach for his Luger'. A Department like the Professor's does have some sort of research record, but as the doctors have to go out and earn money eight days a week, the publication figures are not all that good. Even so, in a research assessment exercise, they have come out a good deal better than those in some departments of other establishments. On the question of space for the conduct of autopsies, the Coroners' Act requires every area and town to provide suitable accommodation. Cities like Sheffield, for example, and the London Boroughs have public mortuaries, whilst others may arrange for rented space in a local hospital. Where the mortuary is so used for coroners' autopsies, a 'Bed & Breakfast' arrangement may exist whereby the coroner pays a rent for each body and each post-mortem that is carried out there.

c)   The third aspect, Quality Assurance is a vital one. Every pathologist on the Home Office List must face the quality assurance test devised by the Home Office Policy Advisory Board's Sub-committee (HOPAB for Forensic Pathology). The Freelancers have to submit as well, but the disciplinary procedures adopted if someone does not meet the standards are so convoluted and archaic that years may pass before a case is worked through the appeal procedure and judicial review. It is known that one or two doctors had their wrist slapped, but no one has as yet been crossed off the List. There is, however, one case of a litigious foreign graduate pending, the outcome of which is eagerly awaited. In the Department of the Professor interviewed, all the facilities for regular meetings (to which other people may be invited) are available, and his staff make sure that their reports, photographs, etc. go across his desk before these leave the building. Likewise, colleagues get to see reports, which together with regular external quality assurance meetings (in which cases are discussed), provide good checks on quality matters. These external meetings are held four times a year and are voluntary. It is of interest to mention that two Independents from the North of England have declined repeated invitations to come and put their photographs on the table and have them discussed. In this way, they submit only to the minimum quality assurance which they are compelled to have but, (says the Professor), they certainly don't go out of their way looking for it. In former years, enlisting a forensic pathologist for the Defence was unheard of. Nowadays the Defence may require a second post-mortem, which (in the experience of one Head of Department) happens in 90% of homicides. The second consultant will look at the first reports and photographs and may ask questions why this or that had not been thought of, although arguments occur more over interpretations than facts. But these checks do make the average forensic pathologist careful about expressing opinions which may later be subject to public peer review in the witness box. This is one aspect to be said in favour of the adversarial system of law in England and Wales. The Two-Doctor Co-operation System in Scotland has no such independent checks and this may possibly be held to affect quality and increase the chances of bias.

A MOSAIC OF FURTHER ISSUES AWAITING RESOLUTION

The discussion in this chapter so far has dealt with a number of trends and problems which continue to give grave concern to leading members of this profession. There are, however, still further issues profoundly influencing the future development of forensic pathology. Let us consider them in turn:

1. Why this specialty is undergoing a **downward spiral** has been made clear already above. At the top, both the Home Office and the Department of Health show a reluctance to accept responsibility for the investigation of death in the community, and that is not just homicide, but death in general. To quote a leading professor in this field: '... *people like Sir Kenneth Calman, the Chief Medical Officer, stand up and make fine speeches about the value of the autopsy for medical and surgical audit, but they make no provision for funds, no adequate arrangements for training posts and they certainly do not ensure that post-mortems are properly conducted. Through the College my colleagues and I, have tried to suggest some form of 'Flying Squad' system which pays surprise visits to hospital*

mortuaries, but this has been opposed at every level by the profession as a whole'.

2. **Slow recruitment**, our Professor explains, has long been a serious concern. *'To go back to the 1980s, someone in the Department of Health decided that too many Histopathologists (see Note 2) and General Pathologists were being trained. This terribly wrong assessment resulted in the under-recruitment of Senior Registrars and Consultants in Hospital Pathology. So, if you have a situation where Hospital Pathology sneezes, Forensic Pathology catches a severe cold. This is because you need a very special sort of person to be a Forensic Pathologist. Most candidates go into pathology as a whole because they are not happy meeting people, they are shrinking violets, and certainly not the sort who are prepared to stand up and fight their corner in Court. You need a certain streak of the prima donna mentality to be a successful Forensic Pathologist and there aren't many of them in Medicine these days as the selection procedure at the undergraduate level has tended to weed quite a lot of them out. Members of the School Debating Society now opt for the Law or go to the Bar rather than Medicine, and we are not recruiting those with 'stage presence' that we used to right down to the age of 18'.*

3. Closely bound up with the staffing problems discussed earlier is the matter of a career structure. There is now in the (so-called) **Calman Report** (1993) this new idea to precede the specialist training by a general grounding in case a forensic pathologist wishes to revert to hospital pathology. But recruits have come to realise that even a two-year period spent in the forensic specialty will cause them to fall off the ladder of a hospital career, which is why they do not join in the first place. The last few candidates in our Professor's Department have already passed their MRC Path in General Pathology and then taken a chance with an option for Forensic Pathology. So far, the professor has managed to place them, but for how much longer he does not know.

4. As far as the reduction or closure of academic departments is concerned, our geographical run-down has shown already what is now happening in the entire area of England and Wales. Suffice it to say that the last 'Established' Chair in the country is based at Sheffield and there is one 'Personal' Chair in Wales. Scotland has

two 'Regis' Chairs in Glasgow and Edinburgh, but they are the only Chairs in the United Kingdom which do not die with their occupants.

5. There is a disparity of working conditions as we have seen and this is bound to affect quality. Here, our Professor quotes what his father used to say: '... *those who have much always want more*'. Many of the Independents take on far more than they can conveniently cope with, both routine Coroners' work and Defence cases, because they are paid piece-work. So it follows that they will produce a three-page report with a lot of deficiencies as opposed to a twelve-page report that a member of the Professor's team would put in. But even in his own Department, for example, there is pressure to cut corners firstly, because the Crown Prosecution Service (CPS) are imposing a very tight time-scale on committal proceedings; and secondly, because he has now to look at the cost of every section (of the body) to assess how few organs he needs to take from each case rather than how many.

6. So to explain the dwindling recognition of the profession's vital role and to avoid confusion, readers are again reminded of the difference between Forensic Pathologists and Forensic Scientists. The former, our main concern in this book and generally known as the 'Medical Detectives', undertake post-mortem examinations of bodies found in 'suspicious circumstances' in order to establish (so far as can be done) the medical cause of death. Forensic Scientists, on the other hand, provide wide-ranging impartial information (usually in a laboratory) from the physical evidence obtained at the scene of crime, such as blood-stained clothes or broken glass. Both professional groups are a part of the Home Office Forensic Services, but both specialties are also in some ways - as in its lack of doctor-patient relationship - somewhat removed from the core of traditionally-viewed medical practice. Our Forensic Pathology professor believes that just lately his group of specialists have suffered on account of the adverse reputation of Forensic Science derived from the cases of the Guildford Four and the Birmingham Six, because of the allegations about contamination and such, so there tends to be an assumption that anyone associated with the term Forensic is either incompetent, bent, or both. Neither are media reports absolved from blame as they generated a sort of public swing against autopsies in general. There is now also far more difficulty about consent for retention material and academic autopsies in

hospitals these days are very rare. He asks why a country where over 75% of bodies are cremated makes such a fuss about taking bits of tissue from the individual cadavers before they are reduced to five pounds of ash. But, as the Professor says, there is now far more opposition, threat and abusive letter encountered than ever before. People don't seem to understand that you need to do a detailed and meticulous post-mortem when investigating a homicide, to establish among other matters whether the effects of pre-existing disease should be excluded.

CONCLUDING OBSERVATIONS

It is as well to remember that a mere 45 forensic pathologists serve the whole of England and Wales. This meant about ten years ago, for example, that very nearly 176,000 deaths were reported by coroners of which some 136,000 (77%) required post-mortem examinations. Suspicious deaths at that time numbered about 1,500, for which the police needed forensic pathologists at the scene. It emerged eventually, that some 630 ended up as recorded homicides. (Wasserman, 1989). (Note: detailed current Home Office statistics will be found in Chapter 3.) This was the time when the Working Party on Forensic Pathology, chaired by Mr. Wasserman, Assistant Under Secretary of State at the Home Office, was in session to review arrangements to provide this service in England and Wales. Its premise was to deal with the organisation and funding of the service, appointments and working conditions, as well as quality assurance and training. Highly qualified doctors in the forensic field were called upon to give evidence and a Policy Advisory Board (PABFP) was set up to include representatives from the Police and Coroners' organisations, the Crown Prosecution Service and leading practitioners from the universities and the National Health Service. After a lengthy period of inactivity, following Mr. Wasserman's retirement (he was asked to re-apply for his job) and a change of Government, the Home Office down-sized the team of civil servants running the Board and Subcommittees to two seniors. After this hiatus of over two years, the latest information from the new Secretary and one of the leaders of the professions is that the corner has been turned and the implementation of the Wasserman proposals is now essentially complete, with work proceeding in the three key areas defined in the terms. The ongoing quality assurance programme is in place. The Home Office continues to give financial support for senior academic posts in departments of forensic medicine and has just instituted a series of training posts to encourage younger doctors to enter this specialism. Also, applications for research funding are invited annually and the advertisements attract a high level of interest.

But such mild optimism is not widely shared in the profession if one looks at the arguments recently presented in the Medico-Legal Journal by the Editor. The Wasserman Report took two years to compile and promised to a worried set of specialists, measures which would put the subject of Forensic Medicine on a more secure footing. Among the proposals (already discussed in earlier chapters) a new structure would provide that the beneficiaries of the service, that is the Home Office, the Police, and Coroners, be charged the 'going rate'. Ten years have slipped by since publication of the report and one finds meanwhile that two out of four academic departments in London have closed. There is no longer a Chair in Forensic Medicine anywhere in the Metropolis where some 50% of the recorded homicides in the country are to be found each year. Moreover, instead of a consolidation and improvement of the remaining departments, the total number of practising forensic pathologists in London has shrunk to about a third. In the UK as a whole, the fragmentation of the specialism through scattered part-time work among local hospital pathology departments, leaves just one solitary Chair located south of Hadrian's Wall. But (the Editorial goes on to inform us) whether by dedication or good organisation, the police can always get a forensic pathologist when they need one if they are prepared to pay the agreed sum per case examination originally proposed by consultants Touche Ross. The article predicts that Forensic Medicine as an academic discipline will not flourish on this basis and some disgruntled members have once more voiced great concern in their endeavour to halt the decline.

What of the future?

Dr. Shepherd (1998) expresses a view on the future of the profession also. Given that the decline of this specialty is of great concern to the Police Force and the Home Office, the PABFP will fund training posts for junior pathologists who are seriously interested in this specialism and who wish to help breathe new life into the subject. This can only happen if academic departments use the funds allocated to forensic medicine for this purpose and not subsume them into a main Police and Home Office Research Fund. As to the Quality Assurance Programme, designed to improve standards within the discipline, it has as yet no teeth; nor has the main Board itself (at the time of writing) met recently to monitor, sustain and promote Forensic Medicine. Much time and effort has already been devoted by the profession to solve the readily perceived problems so elusive of an obvious solution. Are the wrong questions being asked, are the problems being considered in the wrong framework, and need the Coroner's system be changed? Perhaps (suggests Dr. Shepherd) the solution for Forensic Medicine is a direct involvement in all suspicious and sudden deaths, which could be achieved by an overhaul, a reinvigoration of the Coroner's system and a closer incorporation of the pathologists' expertise in the process of investigation. (See note at the end of this chapter).

Reliable sources in the profession reinforce the view that among the many changes during the years since the Wasserman report has been the rise of the NHS Trust hospital in which it is recognised forensic pathology does not easily integrate because such a specialism demands time and is often subject to unpredictable schedules. It is clearly difficult for, say, a histopathologist working on diseased tissues within the NHS to devote part of the time to forensic matters. Furthermore, there is little time left in the medical schools for any serious study of forensic medicine on account of their already crowded curricula and therefore few of them will provide for it. Hence the intractable problem at this time of the small number of young doctors opting for pathology as a career. 'Just skirting around this aspect of medicine is not nearly good enough to make it as a forensic pathologist', a very senior member in the profession suggests. Cynical views for the declining popularity suggest the lack of opportunity for private practice as one significant factor. It is also believed that the tremendous improvements in diagnostic imaging, such as MRI scanning, for example, renders pathology less necessary because accurate diagnostic techniques during one's lifetime are now possible. Some difficulties are now experienced filling consultants' posts in any branch of pathology and manpower planners attribute such recruitment problems to a cyclical path in which simply a low point has been reached.

Those comments may sound a trifle bleak, especially as there are now fewer doctors on the Home Office Register then there were ten years ago, but one observes hopeful indicators also. This specialism is moving more towards a full time status and in total more cases are being examined by fewer than 50 practitioners on the Register. In busy periods manpower crises can occur, and more so if, say, two experienced individuals happen to retire close together. The Wasserman reforms have ensured better funding and the Home Office Policy Advisory Board is actively promoting the development of forensic pathology, as well as helping to arouse new interest in the subject as an academic discipline. Another innovation in the offing will be the setting up of a formal professional register. This step has surprised even the doctors themselves, but has long been campaigned for, says Dr. Rothwell (1999), a former Director of a Home Office Forensic Science Laboratory. It came about after various initiatives including a House of Lords Committee Report which has Government approval that the register should encompass all those involved in the scientific expert witness process. In due course, such a Council for the Registration of Forensic Practitioners in the UK would be expected to include pathologists under its umbrella. If this comes to fruition, it will prevent what is happening now, that anyone can screw a brass plate on his or her front door, stating 'forensic scientist' and be recruited as an expert witness in court. Miscarriages of justice might well be the result.

On the technical side, the areas of toxicology and serology will be subject to a good deal of research and development in the future. Also, new techniques in forensic science are being pioneered all the time and will be accessible to every police force in the country. The example of DNA testing springs to mind in which there has been recently a revolutionary breakthrough by experts in the Forensic Science Service after testing the new technique in secret over the last few months. Past investigations of rape and other crime had to find traces of blood and body fluids, whereas now criminals may be identified by samples from surfaces that have been exposed to the merest touch. DNA can be taken from dead skin cells, minute specks of dried blood, even flakes of dandruff hardly visible to the naked eye. This innovation, made possible by better equipment and computer software, enables scientists to test minute specks of blood containing DNA dating back years, the scientists believe. (Rose, 1999).

Although such technical backup services are of vital importance to the detection of crime, the tools of the forensic pathologist remain his or her eyes, hands and above all, experience. As Dr. Picton (1971) explains:

'...No computer can replace the almost intuitive recognition of some tiny fact by the pathologist who has seen it all before. Experience is something impossible to convey accurately in text books or the most perfect colour-photography. A forensic doctor may know what he or she is looking at means so-and-so, but be unable to enumerate the points which make the decision definite, often to the exasperation of a lawyer in court'.

This doctor gives the example of a dead body found face-down, with a swollen decomposed face and a black eye, identical to that of a blow. But the pathologist, who has seen a few such cases before, can immediately eliminate violence without a lengthy report while he happens to know this, because of a decade or more of experience. It was a great worry to this author when he wrote (and is still true today) that the present generation of crime doctors are getting so thin on the ground as it takes years to train such specialists.

Given the essentially long training and experience of these (so-called) medical detectives, it is widely believed in lay circles, usually from distorted presentations in the media, that the discovery of criminal mortality is their main concern. It may be an eye-opener for readers to learn (from Dr. Picton and other senior specialists) that their most important contribution to the common good is not the comparatively rare murder investigation but the much more frequent elimination of criminal interference in death from accident, suicide and natural reasons such as disease, plus the routine discovery of reliable causes of death in the community, saving much police time and public expense. Unpleasant and revolting work to most people remains the central core, quite often performed in inferior accommodation and conditions of hygiene that need improvement. Also, a good many of a forensic pathologist's tasks are monotonous and gruesome, even sordid, and embrace hundreds of routine cases dealt with in obscurity, far removed from the spurious glamour we see on television.

Note:
The practice of Forensic Pathology in the investigation of sudden death in England and Wales regularly attracts criticism. Despite previous recommendations in the Brodrick Report (1971), little has been done to change the Coroner system. The following points are still of great concern: lack of uniformity among coroners; poor quality of post-mortem examinations; the extent of involvement by mortuary technicians; insufficient funds for further investigations and the poor understanding of medical matters by legally qualified coroners. (Davison et. al., 1998).

Definition Of Medical Terms

MORPHOLOGY
The branch of biology concerned with the form and structure of organisms.

PATHOLOGY
The study of diseases for their own interest, rather than directly with an immediate view to curing them.

ANATOMY
The science which deals with the structure of the body.

PARADIGM
A pattern or model; could also be a stereotypical example; if the subject is the philosophy of science, the paradigm is a very general conception of the nature of scientific endeavour within which a given enquiry is undertaken.

CELLS
In biology, it is the smallest unit of an organism that is able to function independently; can also be any small cavity or area, such as the cavity containing pollen in another.

BIOCHEMISTRY
(also known as biochemy). The chemistry of living things.

HISTOLOGY
The science of the microscopic structure of tissues; also the study of the structure of organs.

HISTOPATHOLOGY
The study of the microscopic structure of diseased tissues.

APPENDIX 2

AN OUTLINE OF CASES REFERRED TO IN THIS BOOK

Case 1 - R. v. James Hanratty, 1962

The A6 Murder Trial in which James Hanratty was accused of murdering Michael Gregston at a lay-by near Bedford was said to be the largest murder trial in British legal history. It ended in February 1962 with Hanratty sentenced to hang, despite his claims of innocence and disquiet amongst some observers of the trial. In this conviction of capital murder there was an appeal on the grounds that the Trial Judge failed to put fully the case of the defence to the Jury and/or failed adequately to sum up the issues raised upon the evidence adduced by the prosecution. The appeal was dismissed. This trial lasted 21 days with over a 100 witnesses. Current reports in the press inform that the family want his body to be exhumed and DNA tested to prove his innocence and clear his name. At the time of writing, a further appeal is on the cards.

References: Pan Book of Dates, 1990, compiled by Gerald Masters.
R. v. Hanratty, Criminal Law Review, 1962, pp. 409-410.

Case 2 - R. v. Dr. Leonard Arthur, 1981

A consultant paediatrician was accused of murdering a Downe's syndrome infant by a drug overdose. The paradox of this case is that counsel for the prosecution and defence, judge and jury alike, all paid tribute to the professional standing and human conscientiousness of the accused doctor. Whilst the proceedings took the form of a murder trial, they were in reality a test case in medical ethics related to what the duty of a doctor is who has charge of a new-born baby severely and irreversibly deformed, whose parents wish him dead. Should such a child be artificially burdened with life and how can such a case be distinguished from less severe cases? Dr Arthur's action was to place the infant on a regime of non-intervention expected to lead soon to his death. Evidence for the defence supported the measure as falling within the professionally accepted limits of paediatric practice. Complications embraced the variables of clinical condition, parental wishes, the treatment administered, as well as accepted professional opinion and the child's independent rights in law. Dr. Arthur was charged, suspended from practising, sent for trial and thereafter allowed to resumed work. The Midwife and colleagues gave evidence for the defence as did a pathologist. Later the evidence was reviewed, the murder charge withdrawn and replaced by a charge of attempted murder. Further evidence was offered by a consultant in perinatal medicine and the case reviewed again. Members of the Downe's Children Association commented in aid of the defence and a Bishop offered a set of ethical principles relevant to the treatment of deformed babies. Public opinion too favoured the doctor who had the support of MENCAP and the Chief Rabbi. The 55 year old doctor was found not guilty of the attempted murder charge of the baby concerned by the jury of six women and six men.

Reference: Times Index Article 1981, p. 734, "Why the Dr. Arthur verdict is right", 6th November 1982, 14a

Case 3 - The Dingo Baby Case, 1980, 1982, 1983, 1984 (Australia) (Chamberlain v. R.)

One evening in the summer of 1980 when campers enjoyed a barbecue near Ayers Rock in the Australian outback, there was a shout: 'a dingo got my baby'. The baby's basket was empty and campers looked everywhere. Police arrived and some witnesses remembered traces of blood around the tent. Days later a child's torn and bloodstained jumpsuit, singlet and nappy were found near the site, but of the 9-week old baby Azaria there was no trace. The event caused much gossip and speculation and the Aborigines living nearby talked of magic and strange happenings. The Chamberlains (parents) were members of the Seventh Day Adventist Church and rumours got around that the baby was sacrificed. Why was clothing found when the child's body had vanished? Nationwide interest in the case caused a coroner later to read out a long document on television to inform two million viewers that the parents were blameless and that Azaria had met her death from the attack of a wild dingo. But curiosity would not stop. New evidence, tracing foetal blood on the clasp of a camera bag owned by the parents and baby hair, prompted a second inquest in 1982. Also, blood had been cleaned away from suspicious areas in the couple's car. In short, the evidence was consistent with the prosecution's allegation that the mother took the baby from the tent to the seat of the car and cut its throat. The coroner considered there was a case to answer and Mrs Chamberlain was sent for trial. By now the 'Dingo' case had attracted worldwide interest. Textile experts thought it to be scissor cuts - not dingo teeth - that damaged the child's clothing. And, the prominent forensic pathologist from London also could not agree upon a wild dog's involvement. Campers and the president of the Dingo Foundation came out strongly in Lindy Chamberlain's defence. The trial was a very emotional event and there seemed to be no motive for the murder. Nor was the evidence conclusive. Independent witnesses confirmed that Lindy was a caring mother. Neither the rumours of a ritual sacrifice nor a dingo snatch was found probable by outsiders. Still, the verdict of the jury was guilty and the sentence imprisonment for life. By this time Lindy had given birth to her second baby in prison but Kahlia was taken from her. However, since Australian justice did not enforce permanent separation of a mother from her child, Lindy was freed on bail pending an appeal and spent some time in an Adventist Church college. In 1983 the appeal was dismissed and Lindy was back in jail. All attempts to get her released failed until sensational new evidence came to light which included a baby's jacket discovered at Ayers Rock. Then in year 1986 yet another inquiry was ordered and Lindy freed pending its outcome. When officials finally declared that whatever the result Lindy would not be sent back to jail, the case ended at last. Eventually, Lindy recorded all her experiences in a book.

References: Book: "Through My Eyes" by Lindy Chamberlain, Heinemann, 1991.
Book Review: Evening Standard, 31st January 1991, p 21.
Lexis Printout, 51 ALR 225.
The Independent, 26th May 1989, 15:4.
Daily Mail World Wide, 30th November 1990, p10.

Case 4 - The Louise Woodward Case in America 1987, 1988, 1999

A British 20-year-old au pair girl, Louise Woodward, faced a 15 year jail sentence after being found guilty of murdering the eight-month old American baby Matthew Eappen. The child died after a skull fracture led to a blood clot in the space between the brain and the outer membrane, for which Louise was said to be responsible through shaking him and banging his head on a hard surface with the same force as a fall from a two-story building. The jury, hearing conflicting evidence from pathologists and brain surgeons paid to give an opinion, ruled that the injury had occurred that day while he was in Louise's care. Experts from the UK criticised the way the postmortem examination was carried out, namely that the pathologist from the Boston State Medical Examiner's Office did not take pictures of Matthew's head, failed to remove the fractured skull bone and discarded vital evidence. Matthew was also found to be anaemic, which suggested he had an old skull injury. As a key prosecution witness such errors by the Medical Examiner could affect the result of the expected appeal in this case. A later trial hinged on the question whether Matthew's skull had been fractured shortly before his admission to hospital or three weeks earlier. The British doctors were confident that Matthew died from the 'rebleeding' of an old injury. Eventually, the trial judge overturned the jury's verdict of second degree murder and substituted a manslaughter conviction. It was a long trial, which affected Judge Zobel so much that he became totally drained and debilitated by the experience. The appeal's outcome saw Louis still guilty under American law of causing an infant's violent death, but that Judge Zobel's decision to reduce the charge is not tantamount to an acquittal (claimed by the prosecution) as the law permitted the Judge to reduce the verdict, said the Appeal Court. It is the first time in the United State that a trial judge overruled the majority verdict of a jury and the Appeal Court supported him in the sense that he had not overstepped his authority. Louise protested her innocence all along and would have no part in a suggested plea-bargaining. But the parents of the boy confirm (at the time of writing) that they will launch a civil action against the au-pair agency, which incidentally assisted Louise with the cost of her defence. The office of the Boston District Attorney has not given up in wanting to stay the Judge's decision and return her to prison on the grounds that he acted like a second jury. The current position is that Louise was set free and allowed to return home. She now works for the law firm that has defended her as she awaits further outcomes of the appeals, including the one for her acquittal.

References: The Times Index, November 1997, p143.
            Daily Mail, 2nd March 1998.
            Daily Mail, 10th March 1998.

Case 5 - The Death of Nurse Helen Smith in Saudi Arabia 1980, 1982

Helen Smith died in a fall from the balcony at the Arnots' flat in Saudi Arabia. Was it an accident or was it murder? The father, Ron Smith, a former policeman set out to investigate, involving over a period of two years, two coroners, a jury, forensic pathologists as well as the Attorney General and the High Court of Appeal. A Danish pathologist said a blow to the head caused death and a pathologist in Jiddah thought it was a case of murder. The father, drawing attention to the autopsy report of a blow to the head, accused Dr. Arnot. New evidence from Holland claimed that there was a fight at a party in the Arnots' house. Ron Smith wanted an inquest into the death which the Attorney General at first rejected but which the court later allowed, costly as it was. As the case proceeded, the Foreign Office admitted a translation error in a document to the coroner. The Home Office pathologist's report was surrounded by secrecy and a new coroner refused an inquest. The jury returned an open verdict which left many questions unanswered and the victim was buried in such a way as to make exhumation impossible for further tests. At the Leed's inquest in 1982 Ron Smith accused Dr. Arnot of Helen's murder and the jury's open verdict was a disappointment to the doctor because it failed to officially put to rest the rumours and innuendo. Richard Arnot will state his case in a book entitled 'Arabian Nightmare', proposed to be published by Allen & Unwin in year 1999.

References: The Times Index, 1980 (p. 1031), 1981 (p954), 1982 (pp. 861, 1005).

Case 6 - John Preece 1973, dealt with in Scottish Courts

On a frosty winter morning in the year end of 1972 the body of an Aberdeen housewife was discovered close to Scottish border country in a wood. It was decided that Scottish jurisdiction should apply when lorry driver John Preece was charged with her rape and murder in the Summer of 1973. He was tried in Edinburgh and convicted by jury majority verdict to imprisonment for life. A subsequent appeal pleading insufficient evidence against him was dismissed. Scientific evidence linked Preece with the dead woman through stains on her clothing, as well as hairs and material fibres found on her. At the time of the appeal, Dr. Clift, the Home office scientist, was savagely criticised for not having stated in evidence that Helen Will, the murdered woman, had the same blood group -A- as Preece. The latter, a 49 year old hailing from Stoke-on-Trent, was freed by the Scottish court on appeal from the life sentence imposed after spending eight years in prison convicted on discredited scientific evidence in 1973. By then his wife had divorced him and he ended up with a meagre ex-gracia payment from the then Secretary of State.

One might here expand on the significant influence and problems associated with forensic science. Apart from the evidence from biological fluids, hairs and fibres, the deceased had stains on her clothing from an individual who was blood group -A- shared by the accused and in addition being a secretor as well. Michelle Eadie, a scientist, explains:

'Within the scientific community, scientific procedures results and analyses are subject to peer review and independent verification. This is done through publication in journals, presentation of papers and the like. If the research is found to be inaccurate or problematic it receives criticism. The problem when science hits the courtroom is that there is no review of this kind placed on the scientific examination procedures, result found and the interpretation placed on these results. This appears to be mainly due to a general acceptance of science and its conclusions by non-scientists, or the perceived aura of scientific certainty. It is the non-scientists whether it be judge, jury, counsel or solicitor, who are the ones called on to critically evaluate the competence of a scientific witness in court. This, along with a lack of understanding of scientific methods and procedures, can lead to unregulated results being used to decide a person's future.'

This lack of knowledge of science on the part of a lawyer working for the accused can mean that questions normally exposing flaws in scientific evidence are not asked. The Preece case is an illustration of this point upon his conviction in 1973 of rape. The most important forensic evidence was that some -A- group blood cells were discovered in semen stains on the woman's underwear. Preece was found to be blood group -A- and one of the relatively select group of people that secretes blood in their body fluids. What was neglected to be exposed at the trial is that the victim was also of blood group -A- and a secretor. Preece was freed on appeal. 'If the lawyer had any forethought of scientific method, a question that would have exposed this would have been pertinent and extremely important to be asked. Indeed, the forensic scientist should have volunteered this information to the court'. (Michelle Eadie, see Internet Web address below).

References: Science on Trial by Michelle Eadie -
              URL:www.meadi~extro.ucc.su.oz.au.
              The Times, 4th February 1982.
              The Mail on Sunday, 11th November 1984.

THE HUMAN GENOME
AND FORENSIC SCIENCE

In the Millennium Year, scientists managed to unveil one of the greatest advances in the history of science. President Clinton and Prime Minister Blair, linked by satellite from a transatlantic conference, described the decoding of the human genome as a truly momentous event in terms of its fundamental implications for health and society. We are today, said the President, learning the language in which God created life and how this wondrous discovery will revolutionise diagnosis, prevention and treatment of most (if not all) human diseases. We know that what parents transmit, together with environmental factors, will influence our shape and our health. We wonder whether we are endowed with long-life genes from branches of the family or share a grandmother's cancer or great-uncle's suspect heart condition. One day this genetic lottery may be replaced by our GP's gene laboratory and tell us what disease potential we have inherited. At present, our insights into the genetic roots of health and disease are still limited, although an international bio-medical research project is in place to study the sequence and map out the whole complement of diverse human genes in the pool. We all store an estimated 60 to a 100 thousand genes; geneticists have by now isolated several thousand, but there is still a long way to go.

These days genes are discovered and analysed within a short time. It took a 9-year search for scientists to find the gene for cystic fibrosis but coordinated efforts some years later (as part of the Human Genome Project) made possible the mapping of the gene for Parkinson's disease in only 9 days. Now, the working draft of the human genome may enable scientists to alert patients to the risk of certain diseases; predict the course of a disease; precisely diagnose disease and match suitable drugs to treat it and finally develop new treatments at the molecular level. Examples of identified genes related to disease include haemorrhagic stroke; diabetes; kidney disease; breast cancer; hereditary skeletal disorders and deafness. Of course, all this expected new power of genetic medicine will require a consideration of related issues, such as the social, legal and ethical implications for society.

In terms of genetic medicine, how does it all work? Of the 75 trillion or so cells in our body, each one containing 46 chromosomes representing a set of the body's blueprint - the human genome. Under a microscope, the chromosomes look like curled-up, thread-like entities, each resembling a ladder-like chain or rungs with chemical substances, collectively known as DNA (DEOXYRIBONUCLEIC ACID). The rungs of the ladder reveal the genetic code. Scientists used a certain mechanism to crack the code. A fragment of DNA is extracted from a chromosome and cloned, not only to produce many copies, but also to partition it up into four chemical substances identified by letters, each marked by coloured dye for recognition. A computer reads the colours and recognises the unique sequence of letters that compose the particular strand of DNA. Stored information will yield a genetic blueprint and enable scientists to learn how some 90% of the genes are arranged to affect the functioning of the human body.

We know that DNA sequencing technology has still some way to go. When that time comes, large DNA segments, even whole genomes, will make possible a precise individual identification. At present, a forensic scientist may scan about 10 DNA regions that differ from person to person and from this data create a profile (known as a DNA fingerprint). The chance of another person to match that profile from a given set of regions is very small. One of the scientists involved in the US Human Genome Programme expressed the view that if used intelligently, DNA identification can be quite effective, provided (a) parts of the DNA sequence that vary the most between humans are used and (b) such parts are large enough to allow for the fact that human mating is not entirely random.

Samples are taken at the crime scene to generate a DNA profile of a person, which may be blood hair, bone, other body tissue and other objects for later scientific analysis. In a recent case, police took the mouth swabs of 3000 men from which forensic experts created a DNA profile of the perpetrator 23 years after the murder. Some additional examples in which DNA uses play a part in forensic identification are: exonerate those strongly accused of a crime; identify victims in catastrophes and crimes; match the donors of organs with recipients in transplants; detect bacteria and other organisms that pollute air, water, food and such; help to establish paternity in family matters; identify endangered species in wildlife; authenticate consumables such as similar-looking foods; discover pedigree for livestock breeds or seeds. The forensic pathologist will clearly be interested whether the cause of death originated from an act of violence or a disease.

Any type of organism can be DNA sequenced. Once a sequence technology progresses further, direct comparisons of large segments, possibly even whole genomes, will make individual identification feasible. DNA profiles identifying a person can be preserved. Such profiles can reveal intimate details about a person: prone to a particular disease, behaviour problems, sexual orientation, illegitimate birth, etc., which clearly allow for discrimination on genetic grounds by insurers, banks, employers, government agencies and other institutions. A suspect may be innocent and may still be chosen for sampling. A person's entire genome may be stored and not destroyed because the law does not require it. Apart from the social and legal considerations, human genetics gives rise to problems strongly connected with medical ethics and morality. Some examples are growing body parts in a laboratory; transplanting cells; cloning humans; reversing the aging process; helping men conceive by the application of 'Dolly' genetics; genetically modifying animals to feel no pain ('Zombies'). Moral questions under current debate are: will the promotion of health be the prime objective of genetic research? Will private companies discovering genes share this knowledge only for money? Will researchers slap patents on genes? Is there a scientific elite running new biology? Should there be some formal control? Will research money dictate what diseases are researched? Will an insurance company refuse a policy if the potential for a fatal disease can be predicted?

Sources consulted:
White House Press Release, June 2000, Pages 1-3 and DNA Forensics, Pages 1-8, both from Internet site www.ornl.gov/hgmis

Medical Research Council: Diving into the Gene Pool: A user's guide to the new genetic medicine, Wellcome Trust, 1996.

BIBLIOGRAPHY

Ackerknecht, E. H. (1953), *On Rudolph Virchow*, University of Wisconsin Press.

Anonymous (1989), "Digging up Argentina's grim past" *Funeral Service Journal*, Vol.104, No.6, pp.43-45.

Ashley, J. (1987), *The Anatomy of a Hospital*, Oxford University Press, Chapters 1 and 12, and pp.121-122.

Ashurst, P. cited by Kingston, P. in *Evening Standard*, 12th December 1989, p15.

Baden, M. (1989, 1995), *Unnatural Death-Confessions of a Medical Examiner*, Warner Books.

Becker, H. et al. (1961), *Boys in White*, University of Chicago Press.

Blair,D. (1974), "Assessment of a Doctor as a Forensic Witness", *The Criminologist*, Vol.9. No.32,p18.

Blau, P. M. et al. (1956), "Occupational Choice: A Conceptual Framework", *Industrial and Labour Review*, Vol 9, No.4, pp.531-43.

Blumer, H. (1962), "Society as Symbolic Interaction", cited by Rose A. M. in *Human Behaviour and Social Processes*, Routledge and Kegan Paul, London.

Brodrick, N. (1971), Reporting on the work of the committee investigating Death Certification and Coroners, Comnd. 4810, *HMSO*.
Note: This report recommended the contentious point (some opinions would say 'impractical') that the provision of the Pathology Service for Coroners should become the responsibility of the NHS. It was also recommended that the choice of pathologist should not be left to the Coroner but given to some 'other authority'. Although the Brodrick Report did not receive universal acclaim, it was considered thorough and many of its recommendations have since been enacted. It was particularly concerned with undetected homicide, but in Prior's view (as discussed in Chapter 5 of his book), focused totally on clinical and legal issues whilst ignoring the processes surrounding the collection of non-medical data, such as biographical and circumstantial.

Cameron, M. (1980), 'The Medico-legal Expert - Past, Present and Future', *Medicine, Science and Law*, Vol.20, No.1, pp 3-13.

Cameron, M. (1973), "Forensic Medicine- Past,Present and Future", *J. Colombo General Hospital*, No.4,pp.59-68.

Cameron, M. (May 1989), personal interview at the London Hospital Medical College, University of London, Turner Street, E1 2AD

Camps, F. E. (1968), *Gradwohl's Legal Medicine*, Chapter 1, pp.1-13, John Wright and Sons, Ltd: Bristol.

Camps, F. E. (1968), "The Medico-legal Expert", *Med. Sci. Law*, No.8, pp.11-14.

Clift, Alan, Dr., Personal Letter to the author, 16 October 1984.

Companion Encyclopedia of the History of Medicine Volume 2,1997, edited by W.F.Bynum and Roy Porter, Women Doctors, pp.890-895,Routledge.

Coroners Act, 1980.
Note: Under the Local Government Act, 1972, the trend to diminish the number of Coroners received a new impetus which resulted in few appointments to large districts with perhaps many hospitals and public mortuaries. Thus the ancient custom for a Coroner to view the body on which he would hold an inquest became difficult and has been found impractical under the 1980 Act. It is now no longer mandatory.

Davison, A.M.et.al. (1998), *Medicine Science and Law 283*, Vol.38, No 4

Dept. of Health (1993), "Hospital doctors' training for the future: the report of the Working Group on Specialist Medical Training", *Calman Report:* London.

Dr.L.(1987), Detailed Reply to Survey Question 2, dealing with why young doctors are reluctant to specialise in this profession.

Drew, P. and Wootton, A. (1988), *Exploring the Interaction Order*, Polity Press: Cambridge, Chapters 1, 2 and 3.

Duckworth, R. The London Hospital Medical College, advised in a personal letter (8th May 1989) that *'at the London, we style Forensic Pathology "Forensic Medicine"*.

Dunn, W. N. (1981), *Public Policy Analysis*, Prentice-Hall, p226.

Durkheim, E. (1902), *De la division du travail social*. translated by Alkan, F. (1933) *The Division of Labour in Society* by Simpson, George, The Free Press of Glencoe: Illinois.

Durkheim, E. (1951), *Suicide: A Study in Sociology*, The Free Press of Glencoe: Illinois.

FEMA-Federal Emergency Management Agency, 500c Street SW, Washington DC 20472 (Info 1999): This agency deals with major disasters in America.

Fulton, R. (1976), *Death and Identity*, Revised Edition, Bowie,Md.: the Charles Press.

Galen, C. G. (130-200), Greek physician and writer on medicine, practised in Rome and was also physician to emperor Marcus Aurelius.

Garfinkel, H. (1974), *Positivism and Society*, Heinemann, pp.54-55.

Garfinkel, H. (1967), *Studies in Ethnomethodology*, Prentice-Hall, p18.

Gee, D. (1998), "Training the Expert Witness", *Medicine, Science and Law*, Vol.28, No.2, pp.93-97 Paper addressed to the British Association of Forensic Medicine.

Ginzberg, E. et al. (1951), *Occupational Choice: An Approach to a General Theory*, Columbia University Press, pp.27 and Chapter 15.

Glaser, B.G. and Strauss, A.L. (1965), *Awareness of the Dying, Aldine*, New York.

Goffman, E. (1981), *Stigma-Notes on the Management of Spoiled Identity*, Penguin Books.

Goffman, E. (1961), *Asylums*, New York, Doubleday Anchor.

Gonzalez-Crussi, F. (1986), *Three Forms of Sudden Death*, Picador, pp.65-70.

Gonzalez-Crussi, F. (1985), *Notes of an Anatomist*, Picador, p65.

Green, M. A. (1987), personal letter in response to mine 13th July 1987.

Green, M. A. (1974), "Forensic Pathology- A Dying Art?", *Criminology*, Vol. 9, No.34, pp.47-50.

Green, M. A., personal letters to the Author, 2nd February, 1990 and 8th May, 1998. Professor and Head of Department of Forensic Pathology, University of Sheffield, Medico-Legal Centre, retired 1999 (currently Consultant Pathologist to the Home Office)

Gresham, A. (1973), *A Colour Atlas of Forensic Pathology*, Wolfe Medical Books, pp.6-7.

Havard, J. D. J. (1960), *The Detection of Secret Homicide*, Macmillan: London.

Hillman, H. (1978), "Death-a Medical Viewpoint", *Attitude to Life and Death*, North East London Polytechnic, Faculty of Environmental Studies.

HMSO (1994), *Report of the Interdepartmental Committee on Medical Schools* (known as the Goodenough Report).

HMSO (1968), *Royal Commission on Medical Education 1965-68, Comnd 3569*, (known as the Todd Report).

HMSO (1987), The Effectiveness of the Forensic Science Service, *Research Study 92* Ramsey Report.

HMSO (1987), A detailed analysis of the case load involving also other than violent offences can be found in the Home Office Research Study 92, The Effectiveness of the Forensic Science Service.

HMSO.14. Committee Report on Death Certification and Coroners(1971), Brodrick Report.

Holland, J. L. (1959)), "A Theory of Occupational Choice", *Journal of Counselling Psychology*, Vol.6, pp.35-45.

Home Office Crime and Criminal Justice Unit, Research Development and Statistics Directorate, 50,Queen Anne's Gate,London SW1H 9AT., Letter and Enclosures dated 4th January 1999.

Houts, M. (1968), *Where Death Delights*, Victor Gollancz.

Hughes, E. C. (1958), *Men and Their Work*, Greenwood Press: Connecticut, pp.44-49, 103-120, 129.

Hunt, A.C. (1989), Derriford Hospital, Histopathologist, personal letter in reply to mine, June 1989.

Hunt, A.C. Personal Letter to the author, 5th November, 1987.

Johnson, H.R.M.,(1969),"The incidence of unnatural deaths which have been presumed to be natural by Coroners' autopsies". *Med.Sci.Law*, No.9, pp.102-106.

Kamerman, J. B. (1988), "Death in the Midst of Life: Social and Cultural Influences on Death", *Grief and Mourning*, Prentice Hall, pp.7-8.

Karsner, H. T. (1946) "Pathology, Old and New", *Bulletin of the New York Academy of Medicine* (2nd series), 22, pp. 371-388.

Kellett, R.J. (1986) *Forensic Medicine- The Crisis in England and Wales*, pp.1-10, (Research Paper sent by him as part of personal correspondence with the author).

King, L. S. and Meehan, M. G. (1973) "A History of the Autopsy", *American Journal of Pathology*, 73, 2, pp. 514-544.

Knight, B. (1987), personal letter in response to mine 30th September 1987.

Knight, B. (1975), "The Defence Pathologist", *The Ciminologist*, Vol.10, Nos. 35/36, pp.12-13,

Knight, B. (1985), "Forensic Pathology: The Chronic Crisis", *British Medical Journal*, Vol.291, No.6503, pp.1145-1146.

Knight, B., (1967), "Decline and Fall", *Journal of the Forensic Science Society*, No. 7, pp.121-122.

Knight, B.,(1980), *Discovering the Human Body*, Heinemann, pp.178-181.

Leadbeatter, S. and Knight, B. (1987), "The History and the Cause of Death", *Med-Sci-Law*, Vol.27, No.2,pp.132-135.

Lexis Printouts 1983/4, on the 'Dingo Baby Case', otherwise Chamberlain and Another v. R., High Court of Australia; and a Write-up in *The Independent*, 26th May 1984, "The Fallibility of Forensic Evidence", Reporter Woffinden, Bob.

Lindley, R. from St Mary's Hospital Medical School, Lecture at Paddington College to Students sitting for the Certificate in Health and Hygiene for the Funeral Services, November 1988.

Mant, K., Personal Letter to the author, 3rd November, 1987.

Mant, K. (1986), "Changes in the Practice of Forensic Pathology, 1950-85" *Med.Sci.Law*, vol.26,No.2, pp.149-157.

Mant, K. (1984), *Taylor's Principles and Practice of Medical Jurisprudence*, Chapter 1, pp.1-14,Churchill Livingstone: Edinburgh.

Mant, K. (1986) "Forensic Medicine: What is its Future?" *American Journal of Forensic Medicine and Pathology*, 7(1),pp.17-22.

Mason, K. (1983), "Coroners across the Border", *Med-Sci-Law*, Vol.23.pp.271-4.

Masters, B (1991) "The Devil in Us All", *Evening Standard*, 7th March 1991 p7.

Mead, G. H. (1934), *Mind, Self and Society*, University of Chicago Press.

Merton, R. K., (1957), *The Student Physician*, Harvard University Press, p. 287.

Miller, D. C., and Form, W. H., (1964), *Industrial Sociology: The Sociology of Work Organisations*, Harper and Row, pp.466-467.

Musgrave, P.W. (1974), "Towards a Sociological Theory of Occupational Choice", *Occupational Choice*

Orwell, G. (1970), *Down and Out in Paris and London*, Penguin.

Park, R. H. (1928), "Human Migration and the Marginal Man", *American Journal of Sociology*, vol 33, May 1928, pp.881-893.

Pereira, M., quoted in Phillips, J.'s Paper of 1983 on the Clift Case.

Phillips, J. (1983), "A Winter's Tale - the Slings and Arrows of Expert Evidence", *Law Institute Journal*, July 1983, pp.710-713.

Picton, B. (1971) *Murder, Suicide or Accident*, Robert Hale: London.

Plummer, K. (1985), *Encyclopedia of Sociology*, Macmillan, pp.348-349.

Prior, L. (1987), "Policing the Dead: A Sociology of the Mortuary", *Sociology*, Vol. 21, No.3,pp.355-376.

Prior, L. (1989), *The Social Organisation of Death*, Macmillan, Chapters 1, 5, 8 and 9, pp 9-10, 19, 154-156, 199, 371-373.

Reals, W. J. and Cowan, W. R., (1979) *Forensic Pathology and Mass Casualties in Human Pathology*, Vol. 10, No.2, pp.133-136.

Roberts, K. (1975), "The Development Theory of Occupational Choice", cited in Esland, G., et al, *People and Work*, Open University Press.

Roger, P.D. and Hillman, H. (1970), "The Increased Recovery of Spontaneous Respiration in Rats following Profound Hypothermia", *Journal of Applied Physiology 29*, pp.58-63.

Rose, A. M. (1965), *The Study of Human Relations*, Knopf, p.151.

Rose, P. (1999) "Chief Crime Correspondent", *Daily Mail*, p.2, 31st May.

Rothwell, T. personal letter to the author, 22nd April,1999.

Sakinofsky, I., Letter to the Editor on "Suicide in Doctors and their Wives", *British Medical Journal*, 2nd August, 1980, p.386.

Saunders, K. (1979), Case Study deals with Hospital Porters' ambivalent identity, not included in this book. See also article "The Hospital Porter: A Behavioural Profile of an Occupation in the World of the Care of the Sick", *Employee Relations*, Vol. 1. pp.30-32.

Saunders, C. (1981), *Social Stigma of Occupations: The Lower Grade Worker in Service Organisations*, Gower.

Seeman, M. (1959), "The meaning of Alienation", *American Sociological Review 24*, p.783.

Selzer, R. (1981), *Mortal Lessons: Notes on the Art of Surgery*, Chatto and Windus, London, pp.209-216.

Shepherd, R. (1998) "Turn Out the Light and Shut the Door", *Medico-Legal Journal* 1, 1-2 Editorial

Shepherd, R. (1990), "Disaster Management" (Editorial), *Medico-Legal Journal*, 58(1), pp.3-4.

Simpson, C.K. (1963), "The Changing Face of Forensic Medicine 1930-1960", *Guy's Hospital Reports* 112,pp.338-344.

Smyth, F. (1980), *Cause of Death: A History of Forensic Science*, pp.24-33. Pan Books, London Orbis Publishing Ltd.

Sudnow, D. (1967), "Dead on Arrival", *Trans-Action*, Vol.5,pp.36-43.

Super, D.E. et al. (1957), *Vocational Development: A Framework for Research*, Teachers College, p.156 (see Reference 7 in this Chapter).

The Times, 11th April 1984 (DC). "R.v.West Yorkshire Coroner, ex parte Kenyon".

Virchow, R. (1858) *Cellular Pathology*.

Wasserman, Gordon J., Assistant Under Secretary of State, Home Office, then Chairman of the Working Party on Forensic Pathology and author of the HMSO April, 1989 Report.

Wecht, C. H. (1977), "Forensic Pathology - A Speciality in Trouble", *The New England Journal of Medicine*, 297,22, pp. 1232-1234.

WHO, (1978), *Medical Certification of the Cause of Death*, World Health Organisation, Geneva.

Whyte, W. (1948), *Human Relations in the Restaurant Industry*, McGraw-Hill.

Wilensky, Harold L., (1964), 'The Professionalisation for Everyone', American Journal of Sociology 70 (September 1964), pp. 137-158.
Note: A recent tale from a Senior Pathologist refers: he knows of a mortuary at which technicians were busy extracting organs from some thirty bodies on slabs. Then the professor enters, makes the rounds from slab to slab to inspect the work. As he is said to be paid £40 for each of the bodies, has earned £1200 within the hour. This story could not, however, be verified.

Wilkins, R. (1990), *The Fireside Book of Death*, Robert Hale.

Williams, R. (1989) *Journal of the Forensic Science Society*, Vol.29, No.1,pp.1-3.

Williams, W. M. (1974) Editor, *Occupational Choice* (Chapter 11 refers), Allen and Unwin.

Wolbach, B. S. (1954), "The Glorious Past, the Doleful Present and the Uncertain Future of Pathology", *Havard Medical Alumni Bulletin*, pp. 45-48.

Wonder, A. (1989) "Science and Law, a Marriage of Opposites", *Journal of the Forensic Science Society*, Vol.29, No.2, pp.75-76.

INDEX